Amber

Butterworth Gem Books
Edited by Peter G. Read

Amber
Helen Fraquet

Beryl
John Sinkankas and Peter G. Read

Garnet
John D. Rouse

Jet
Helen Muller

Pearls: natural, cultured and imitation
Alexander E. Farn

Quartz
Michael O'Donoghue

In preparation

Corundum
Richard W. Hughes

Diamond
Roy V. Huddlestone

Opals
P. J. Darragh

Topaz
D. B. Hoover

Butterworths Gem Books

Amber

Helen Fraquet

Butterworths
London Boston Durban Singapore Sydney Toronto Wellington

First published 1987

© **Butterworth & Co (Publishers) Ltd. 1987**

British Library Cataloguing in Publication Data
Fraquet, Helen
    Amber.——(Butterworths gem books)
    1. Amber
    I. Title
    553'.29   QE391.A5
    ISBN 0-408-03080-1

Library of Congress Cataloging in Publication Data
Fraquet, Helen.
    Amber.

    (Butterworths gem books)
    Includes bibliographies and index.
    1. Amber. I. Title. II. Series.
    QE391.A5F73 1987   553.2'9   87–811
    ISBN 0-408-03080-1

Typeset by Latimer Trend & Company Ltd, Plymouth
Printed and bound in Great Britain by Butler & Tanner Ltd.,
Frome and London

Preface

This book is an amber primer. The subject of fossil resins is so vast, and covers so many different sciences, that no single facet can be covered in depth in a work of this size. I hope therefore that, having read this book, readers will seek out the specialist references given at the end of each chapter, for there is a wealth of research currently being undertaken on this subject and, if nothing else, this text will serve as an introduction to that research.

The gemmologist is expected to analyse and categorize amber, usually with no provenance and in an altered state from natural. At its simplest the question may be to decide whether a necklace is made of an early plastic or a natural resin; at a more complex level, infra-red spectroscopy may be employed to differentiate between a carving of succinite or simetite resins.

Unlike other sciences such as entomology or archaeology, gemmology is closely allied to commercial considerations. The resin is usually being questioned because of an insurance valuation, or a query that has arisen at auction. Speed of decision is a necessity, and it is for this reason that I have placed, for example, plastics in a separate section. In short this book is what I, as a gemmologist, found lacking when I started working on amber 15 years ago. There are still gaps even in our basic knowledge – a great deal of work needs to be carried out for instance on Chinese carving, the historical use of amber in Central and South America, the ethnographic importance of amber, copal and now plastic in Africa – and I look forward, following the publication of this volume, to benefiting from the wealth of information that there is among its readers.

Helen R. Fraquet

Acknowledgements

Those who remember the heyday of rare ornamental ambers – from Burma, Romania and Sicily – are dwindling fast in number. Authors of classic books on amber, like Göppert, Menge and Conwentz in the nineteenth century, and Rhode in the first half of this century, passed on long before I was born. The great collector Kitson and the Charatan brothers, of Sac Frères in Bond Street, died while I was at school.

However, the year I left school I was introduced, by a collector of oriental amber carvings, to Rosalind Denny MBE, an old lady who had spent her life researching amber but who had never published her work. We were both obsessed with this fossil resin, and I am afraid she had much to put up with from my youthful opinionating. Today some of her notes have been incorporated here, especially in the chapters concerning Oriental and Sicilian ambers. Miss Denny instilled a discipline into my quest for knowledge, for which I am eternally grateful.

Over the past 15 years many people have shown me extreme kindness, by passing on their papers, or letting me view their private collections.

However, special thanks must go to Alan Jobbins, past Curator of Minerals and Gemstones, Geological Museum, London, for his encouragement throughout this time, and to those who have given me guidance over specific chapters in this book:

Jørgen Jensen, National Museum, Copenhagen; Stephen Shennan, University of Southampton; Majorie Trusted, Victoria and Albert Museum, London; C.A. Redfarn, Redfarn and Bedford, Consulting Chemists, London; Eduardo Fecarotta, Fratelli Fecarotta, Catania; Georg Dommel, Ambar del Caribe, Dusseldorf; Dieter Schlee, Staatliches Museum für Naturkunde, Stuttgart; Gheorghe Vasilescu and Amuliu Proca, Enterprise for Geological and Geophysical Inspections, Bucharest; Pompelio and Salvador Brouwer, Santo Domingo; Neil Hanna, New Zealand Gemmological Association; Paul Whalley, Ed Jarzembowski, Gary Jones and Eileen Bruton, British Museum (Natural History); Stephen Briggs, Trefenter Llangwyryfon; Ken Scarratt, London Gem Testing Laboratory; and the staff of the Royal Botanic Gardens, Kew.

Lastly, thanks must go to Helen Muller, author of the Butterworths Gem Book on

Jet, who approached me to write this book, and to John Rooke, who has taken so many of the photographs, and shown much patience in sharing our house with an ever-increasing collection of fossil resins and their associated papers.

Dedication

To John and Emma, with love.

Contents

Chapter 1

Profile: summary of characteristics

Amber is a resin that has fossilized and lost many of its volatile component fractions.

Crystal system:	Amorphous, but may contain crystalline phases.
Chemical composition:	Varies; mean values given: carbon 78.8%, hydrogen 10.2%, oxygen 11.0% (Schrotter, 1843), carbon 78.6%, hydrogen 10.5%, oxygen 10.5%, sulphur 0.4% (Helm, 1891)
Optical character:	Isotropic; however, shows considerable interference under polarized light due to internal strain. This is especially so of ambroid or pressed amber
Refractive index:	1.54 (singly refractive)
Specific gravity:	1.08
Hardness:	2–2½ on Mohs' scale, burmite being the hardest, Dominican the softest
Cleavage:	None
Fracture:	Conchoidal. Some clear golden ambers of nineteenth-century Chinese workmanship appear to fracture very cleanly along lines of weakness not visible to the human eye (this is not to be confused with the natural construction of 'shelly amber'). Romanian ambers are often splintery on fracture due to an already shattered internal composition
Lustre:	Resinous. Some softer Dominican amber is waxy. Due to oxidation, amber alters once it is exposed. Initially pale osseous ambers acquire a thin clear layer like porcelain. In time, all ambers suffer surface deterioration to such an extent that the then rusty-red crust crumbles away, exposing a new surface which will undergo the same process. This is halted to a large extent if the amber is kept in dark, damp surroundings such as are found underground
Colour:	*Opaque* – white, lemon, golden, red-brown. Brown and vir-

tually black varieties largely due to minerals like iron pyrites, sulphuric acid in solution, or included organic matter.

Clear – colourless, pale yellow, 'sugar syrup' to 'rich sherry', pale scarlet-red, bright red, deep red to almost black.

Very occasionally opaque or clear green. Blue amber (not fluorescent amber) is somewhat of a misnomer. This amber is a marginal blue or grey, between opaque amber and crystals of iron pyrites.

Great care should be taken with all opaque ambers of an unusual colour. On heating they often become clear golden in tone. This effect is irreversible

Fluorescence: Many ambers fluoresce naturally under daylight, especially when freshly extracted. This effect appears to diminish with time, so today will most commonly be encountered in freshly mined specimens from the Dominican Republic. Tones of fluorescence: deep blue, mid-blue, purple and green. This fluorescence is seen by reflected light.

Ambers generally show a powder-blue fluorescent bloom under ultraviolet illumination

Infra-red light: Used spectroscopically to obtain analytical data, especially to 'finger print' resin types.

X-rays; Amber is transparent to X-rays, but some crystalline components may give rise to diffraction patterns

Static electricity: Amber becomes negatively charged when rubbed, picks up small scraps of tissue paper, etc. (*Note:* so do many imitations of amber)

Thermal and electrical conductivity: Very poor. Amber feels warm to the touch and is sometimes used as a thermal insulator

Thermoplasticity: Amber melts at 350–380°C

Included matter: Organic – flora and fauna; inorganic – minerals, liquids and gases.

Back in the last century over 100 fossil resins were named, and this has confused the overview for it is now thought that many resins, fossil or otherwise, share the same botanic parentage. 'There is nothing in literature to indicate that "Ajkaite" found at Ajka in Hungary is in fact different from "Walchowite" found at Litezko near Walchow in Moravia' (Beck, Wilbur and Meret, 1964). Amber from Chiapas, Mexico and that from the Dominican Republic would also appear to show strong affinities, not just for each other but also, from included matter, to the modern tree *Hymenia courbaril* (Schlee, 1984).

Only a few fossil resins are of interest to the gemmologist, these being what is loosely termed *Baltic* amber or succinite (this amber containing between 3 and 8% succinic acid on dry distillation), *Rumanian* amber or rumanite, *Sicilian* amber or simetite, *Burmese* amber or burmite, and ambers from *Mexico* and the *Dominican Republic*. Rumanite and simetite also contain some succinic acid; indeed, succinic acid (*Figure 1.1*) is now thought by some to be merely a side-effect of ageing and oxidation (Rottländer, 1970), but the gemmologist classifies them separately because they were used as a source material for jewellery at quite distinct periods in history. Style and provenance are of no value as strict scientific data, but they are useful pointers to those working in a wider field.

Figure 1.1 Succinic acid crystals, average length between 2 and 3 mm.
Courtesy London Gem Testing Laboratory

Gemmology and ethnography are possibly the only disciplines where amber is first classified by location rather than by the chemical analysis of the resin. This is because man, who collects or works the resin, usually has no scientific interest in the material but rather a commercial interest as to aesthetic beauty and financial value. For example, amber from the Dominican Republic is currently flooding the market. This amber encompasses at least three resins of differing ages and possibly differing botanical parentage. The fact that there are several resins from this one source has only come to the notice of gemmologists because, even in a short period, they clearly react differently from each other, one quickly becoming dull, another becoming very brittle, etc.

Among other sciences there are many learned papers concerning the use of the terms Baltic amber or succinite, or amber containing succinic acid (Broughton, 1974; Savkevich, 1981; Beck, 1982). To the gemmologist what is important is that fossil resin originally formed in the area of the Baltic is not the *only* resin that may be termed amber (a view marketed by Germany for many years, and indeed a curious one as the rarer ambers from other countries have always been more costly to the purchaser). The term *retinite* should also be discontinued as it does not fit today into our more comprehensive knowledge of a wide variety of fossil resins.

Bibliography

BECK, C. W., 'Physical methods used to determine the geological origin of amber and other fossil resins; some critical remarks: comment', *Physics and Chemistry of Minerals*, **8** (1982)

BECK, C. W., WILBUR, E. and MERET, S., 'Infra-red spectra and the origin of amber', *Nature*, **201** (1964)

BROUGHTON, P. L., 'Conceptual frameworks for geographic-botanical affinities of fossil resins', *Canadian Journal of Earth Science*, **11** (1974)

HELM, O., *Schriften Ges. Danzig*, **7**, No. 4 (1891)

LANGENHEIM, J. H., 'Amber: a botanical inquiry', *Science*, **163** (1969)

ROTTLÄNDER, R. C. A., On the formation of amber from Pinus resin, *Archaeometry* **12** (1970)

SAVKEVICH, S. S., 'Physical methods used to determine the geological origin of amber and other fossil resins; some critical remarks', *Physics and Chemistry of Minerals*, **7**, No. 1 (1981)

SCHLEE, D., 'Bernstein – Neuigkeiten', *Stuttgarter Beiträge zur Naturkunde*, **C**, No. 18, Staatliches Museum für Naturkunde, Stuttgart (1984)

SCHROTTER, A., 'Uber mehrere in Braunkohlen- und Torflagern vorkommende neue harzinge Substanzen, und deren Verhlältniss zu einigen Harzen noch lebender Pflanzen', *Poggend. Annal*, **LIX** (1843)

Chapter 2

The use of amber in antiquity

Palaeolithic (450 000–12 000 BC)

Amber, or fossil resin, is first associated with man in Palaeolithic times. Unworked lumps have been found carried into dwelling caves at the Grotte d'Aurensan in the Hautes Pyrenees, at Judenes in Austria, at Kostelik and Zitmy in Moravia and at Cioclovina in Romania.

It will be noticed that all these finds occur in southern Europe, far from the major source of the Baltic. It is thought that these pieces are either erratics, or curiosities found further north by the hunters and carried southwards to the caves. Man at this time is known to have lived a life similar to that of the Eskimo people, and to have covered many miles in the summer months in pursuit of migrating animals.

The southern boundaries of the natural occurrence of Baltic amber coincide with the limits of glaciation. Amber has been found from Palaeolithic times in Britain in Gough's cave (Tratman, 1950).

The attraction of this strange substance to primitive man is an obvious one. Its brilliant colour, lightness of weight, warmth to the touch and the fact that when rubbed it attracts other objects, recommend it highly as an amulet, with magical powers.

Mesolithic (12 000–4000 BC): nomadic hunters

In the Baltic countries there is no trace of any real settlement in the major part of the Palaeolithic for ice still covered much of the country. However, with the thaw, hunters moved northwards following the reindeer, and there is evidence that Mesolithic man used stone, bone, wood and amber.

The climate was initially arctic, the land barren, but gradually the temperature improved and forests became established. The reindeer made way for elk, red deer, aurochs and boar.

Against all odds, an amber pendant carved by one of these ancient hunters has survived (*Figure 2.1*). Still pristine yellow, having been preserved in a bog, it is carved on one side with geometric fringes but on the other are incised five or six figures. The pendant was found in 1959 near the Halleby River, West Zealand, Denmark. The human figures are geometric, but there is no doubt as to what they represent. One can only be awe-struck by the age of this worked pendant.

Figure 2.1 Amber pendant depicting human figures. From the Mesolithic period. Found in West Zealand, Denmark.

Decorations of cross-hatching, V-shaped incisions, drilled series of dots, rhombs, etc. may be either purely of artistic merit or may have been used for counting devices or tallies. It has been postulated that the phases of the moon and the seasons for hunting are recorded on some of these Mesolithic artefacts.

Representations in amber of the animals that these hunters sought are the oldest three-dimensional works of art in northern Europe. They date from about 7000 BC and first occur in Denmark. Stylistically, although they are thought to occur over several thousand years, spreading eastwards, they show a remarkable continuity of design.

These carvings are made from large pieces of amber, the mean being 10 cm in length, so they must have been of great importance. In Denmark, examples include an elk with a goatee beard, a bear and a water-bird. As with the earlier pendant, they are in a remarkable state of preservation, surface oxidation being minimal (*see Plate 1a*).

Until the Second World War, there were other examples stretching east along the Baltic coast to the USSR. However, many were lost in the war and today reconstructions have been made in their place. A bear was found in Stolp, an elk or pony was found in Woldenburg near Berlin and a boar, possibly unfinished, was found near Danzig (Gdansk).

In the extreme east, at Juodkrante (Schwarzort), over 400 Stone Age artefacts were dug up during the nineteenth century by people looking for raw amber. It is now thought that these items originated several thousand years later than the similar objects found in Denmark, but hunting animals are represented among these finds (Jensen, 1982).

Also found at Juodkrante, probably by accident as it appears that this hoard is the result of wave action washing out a series of ambers over a period of time and depositing them all together, are some curious flat human figures. These have bore holes and guide-lines so that they can be sewn on to a garment. Once again, we have only reproductions to study (*Figure 2.2*).

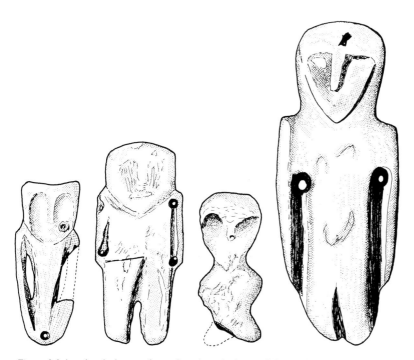

Figure 2.2 Amulets in human form, found washed-out of the original strata at Juodkrante, Lithuania. Mesolithic.

From the last period of the Mesolithic, about 5000 BC, there is a pendant in Denmark marked with a pattern of netting. It is known that the supply of wild animals to hunt was dwindling while the waters of the Baltic were becoming salty. Was this a talisman associated with fish rather than mammals?

Neolithic (4000–1900 BC): the first farmers

The shortage of animals to hunt became so acute that man had to evolve new methods of survival. Fields were cultivated for the first time by Neolithic man, cereals introduced, and evidence of a community rather than individuals becomes apparent from gathering houses where ceremonies were performed, women swapped and strategy developed.

Figure 2.3 shows the general distribution of amber during this period. Finds include large ceremonial sacrifices of amber in household clay pots, probably to evoke good harvests and plenty of food. The amounts of amber are so large – 13 000 beads found at Mollerup in 1940 weighing 4 kg, and 4000 beads at Laesten weighing 8 kg – that organized collection must have taken place throughout the winter storms. This collecting must have extended to some form of barter or gift-giving. A clay pot of 3500 BC, with 300–400 amber beads and also containing copper rings and twisted coils, was found in 1958 at Aarupgaard, near Horsens. Copper is not a metal native to Denmark, and evidence of its occurrence at this early date is surprising. A fragment of a bead from a Neolithic site at Baigneurs à Charavines, Isère, France is dated 2400–2300 BC, complementing these finds (Beck and Bocquet, 1982).

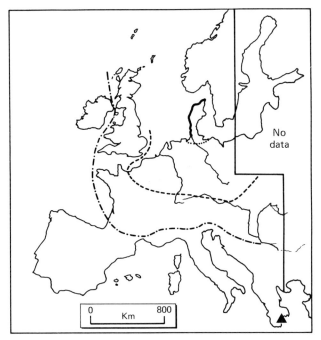

Figure 2.3 Generalized distribution of amber in western and central Europe during the Neolithic and Bronze Age.
The heavy line along the west coast of Jutland indicates the main amber source area in the western Baltic.
······Approximate southern boundary of amber distribution *c.* 2500 BC;
––––Approximate southern boundary of amber distribution *c.* 1900 BC;
·–·–·–·–Approximate southern boundary of amber distribution *c.* 1300 BC.
Triangle marks position of Mycenae. *Courtesy of Stephen Shennan, University of Southampton.*

Often the amber is highly polished and has obviously never been worn. To the gemmologist one of the fascinating things about these beads is the prevalence of dark red, clear amber with internal sun spangles. This effect occurs very rarely in natural Baltic amber but can be induced by heating. Did Stone Age man have this knowledge or is this some by-product of ageing?

Amber beads are also found in the burials of these early farmers, but not in the huge numbers of the sacrificial hoards. An example is of a grave on Zealand at Dragsholm where a young man of about 20 was buried with his battleaxe, arrows and 52 pieces of amber. The latter were spread among five items of jewellery: a necklace, several beads once sewn on to his sleeves, six large beads once sewn across his chest and, at his hips, small amber plates alternating with larger drop-shaped beads. The garments worn by Neolithic man were therefore surprisingly decorative. Already, at this early date, the necklaces contain spacer beads which carry several strings of smaller beads. These are generally beads rather than flat plaques associated with the Bronze Age.

Much of the amber found in offerings and burials is in the form of amulets for axes or double axes, but the peaceful coexistence of the community still retained great importance. In later farming communities, if the men kept cattle they were accorded higher status, whereas in communities where agriculture was the mainstay the women appear to have had the higher status.

Although much of the foregoing has concentrated on Denmark, at about 3000 BC there appears to have been a flourishing industry in the manufacture of amber items on the other side of the Baltic at the Lubanner Lakes, Lithuania. Many half-finished items have been found at this site, and one circular disc with a cruciform design has even found its way to Denmark. Discs, some plain and some with the cruciform design, appear widely in that millennium.

The appearance of the surface grave culture after 2800 BC in Denmark led to radical changes. The use of bronze for the first time coincides with the appearance of ceremonial axes made of amber.

Mediterranean cultures

Lumps of fossil resin are common in ancient Egyptian graves of all periods, particularly those of Badarian, Predynastic and Early Dynastic date (Lucas and Harris), but in reality these are probably local resins as this substance was used to fumigate the tombs. Only in the XVIII Dynasty did amber in the stricter sense reach Egypt.

Amber may have been found in Anatolia and Mesopotamia, the latter in the second and third millennia BC, but there is a lack of positive identification. However, in Mycenaean Greece influxes of amber appear in 1600 BC, 1500 BC and 1200 BC, and it is these ambers that are now discussed in more depth.

The Mycenaean Culture

The arrival of bronze in northern Europe coincides with the first notable appearance of amber in Mediterranean cultures, and recent investigations using infra-red spectroscopy have shown that the vast majority of these ambers are of Baltic origin. Amber appears quite suddenly in the Peloponnese shaft graves of Mycenaean Greece. The number of pieces, mostly biconical beads, is high: 1290 in shaft grave IV alone.

The design of the beads and their rough nature, even allowing for poor conservation, indicate that they were imported as beads, not worked locally; other gems of this period, namely cornelian and amethyst, show a far greater degree of skilled workmanship. As these ambers are found along the coast at the major population centres, it is probable that they crossed Europe by way of the major rivers, like the Rhine and the Rhone, and were then exported locally from Lipari. The key to the trade route may come from the few atypical beads, the most prolific of which are spacer plates.

Spacer plates

Spacer plates from this period have been found throughout Europe: on eight sites in Britain, one in Denmark, seven in France, two in Czechoslovakia, two in Austria and 31 in Germany. However, the picture is clarified as there are some variants which occur in only one or two of these countries. The majority of German plates are designed for crescentric necklaces, while the complex V-boring plate appears only in Britain and in Mycenaean Greece (*Figure 2.4*). The first two eras of Mycenaean finds (1600 BC and 1500 BC) synchronize with relevant graves of the Wessex Culture in Britain. According to Harding and Hughes-Brock (1974), 'There is nothing to indicate that the Greek and British spacers are not of identical origin'. This view is disputed by others, and no doubt research will continue.

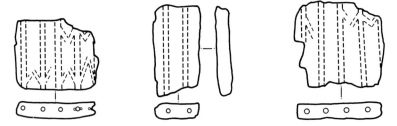

Figure 2.4 Spacer plates, showing internal construction. These were used to separate strings of smaller beads.

The manufacture of spacer plates came to an end in Britain in 1500 BC, and while in Germany the trend continued for another hundred years, these later spacers do not appear in Greece.

The Wessex Culture

The Wessex Culture flourished from *c*.2000 to 1400 BC, its importance originating from the location of Wessex with regard to large ceremonial monuments in the preceding late Neolithic period.

   Little is known about the people of this culture. Their society was hierarchical, their wealth was concentrated in the hands of a few, and their burials contained rich grave goods such as copper daggers, stone battleaxes and attractive personal ornaments, which may not have been of local manufacture. The richest graves were found in the area of southern Britain known as Wessex, one of the first to be developed agriculturally, and the proximity of the monument of Stonehenge may also have played a part in the location of these barrows.

The grave goods reflect the prestige of the occupant: manual tools are seldom found, and in Britain two, or possibly three, examples of the most outstanding amber objects of this period have survived.

Amber beaker-shaped cups*

The most outstanding example of an object made of amber is a beaker-shaped cup which came from a tumulus in Hove. Part of the mound had been removed in the early nineteenth century to make way for a railway station, and in 1857 the remainder was cleared for building work. During this second period workmen came upon an oak coffin, hollowed out of a single tree and shaped with an axe. It measured between 1.8 and 2.1 m in length, and was placed roughly east–west. The wood of the coffin crumbled and the bones were much decayed. It could not be determined with any certainty whether the body itself had been cremated, as a commemorative feast had also taken place in the vicinity, leaving behind much charred debris.

In the centre of the coffin, as if resting on the breast of the body, lay a cup of red amber, a boat-shaped axe of Scandinavian type, a whetstone amulet with touches of red paint, and a bronze dagger with the remains of a wooden handle. The cup is formed from one lump of amber (*Figure 2.5*). It is hemispherical and measures 6.4 cm high × 8.9 cm wide, with a capacity of about a quarter litre. The only decoration is a

Figure 2.5 Amber cup from the grave at Hove, England. *c.* 1500 BC. *Courtesy Brighton Museum.*

*Not to be confused with Bell Beaker pots.

band of five raised lines, about 1 cm below the lip. The cup was turned on a pole lathe as the handle forms part of the whole and is not a later addition. Carbon-14 dating carried out on a knot of wood from the coffin places the burial around 1500 BC.

The survival of the cup is remarkable, for in Medieval times it was traditional for the young to dance on the tumulus. This was linked to Palm Sunday and Good Friday but no doubt had its origins with the Saxon goddess Eostre (Curwen and Curwen, 1924).

In 1882, fragments of a deep brown amber cup were found in Clandown barrow near Dorchester. This cup measures 10.2 cm × 7 cm, and was found beneath two later burials in a cairn of flints. With the amber cup (which was broken in fragments) were a bronze dagger, a diamond-shaped gold ornament finely decorated with incised parallel lines and a jet ornament with three gold knobs (possibly the head of a sceptre). Below the cairn were broken pieces of pottery from an incense cup and a badly broken urn holding the ashes of cremation.

A third amber cup is cited in a work by King in 1860: 'A large amber cup, holding half a pint, has lately been discovered in a tumulus in Ireland', but the author has not been able to locate any more details about this cup.

A gold cup, 8.9 cm high, has been found at Rillaton in Cornwall, England and two others made of shale or Kimmeridge clay have been found in the south-west.

It has been suggested by Harding that the amber used for the cups was of local (i.e. East Anglian) origin. This seems unlikely as there was no history of advanced amber carving on the east coast of England during the Bronze or Iron Age. Indeed, there are only two finds from this period of amber from the east coast: these are the necklaces from the rich barrow at Little Cressingham, Norfolk and those from Rochford, Essex. As the local British amber is identical in composition to Baltic amber, there are no analytical tests that would help solve the question of origin. Finds of amber from the late bronze age are in the main fairly large necklaces of graduated beads, from Ireland and western Britain. They are usually in hoards or isolated finds; in Ireland, they are often found in peat bogs.

Other exotics found among the amber beads of Mycenaean Greece also show evidence of long-distance trade.

A gold-bound disc was found at the tomb of the Double Axes, Isopata ridge, on Knossos. The diameter of the amber plaque is 25 mm with a gold band of 5 mm. Amber discs from Manton Barrow in Wiltshire are similar but the ratio of amber to gold is different – 26:7 mm and 12:13 mm.

Ring pendants, figures of eight and triple circle pieces have been found at Kakovatos, and from the grave robbers' hoard known as the Tiryns Treasure (1200 BC) come barrel-shaped amber beads with large waists, and four curious wheels or nests of gold wire. These are similar to gold ornaments from Hradec Králové, Czechoslovakia.

The Iron Age: classical cultures

Throughout the Iron Age of the south and classical cultures, the Phoenicians were the dominant sea traders. In the ninth century BC, the Assyrians marched westwards towards the Mediterranean and demanded tribute from the rich Phoenicians. Supposedly from this contact we have two extraordinary amber statues of the Assyrian King Ashurnasirpal (*Figure 2.6*). Both statues appeared on the market in the USA under mysterious circumstances, and it is most unlikely that they are originals.

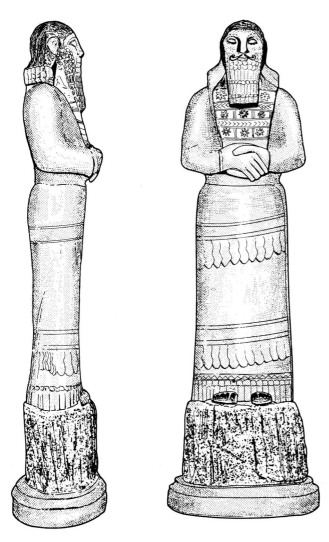

Figure 2.6 Amber statuette of the Assyrian King Ashurnasirpal. Supposedly ninth century BC, found on the Banks of the River Tigris. Height, 20 cm.

However, their existence has puzzled researchers for many years, and feelings as to their originality or otherwise are disputed by various learned authorities. With the advent of infra-red spectroscopy, at least one element of the mystery has been decided. One statue is made of Baltic amber and the other possibly of a local fossil resin from the Middle East.*

*The Boston Assyrian figure was tested by Professor R. C. Lord of MIT, the second figure was tested by C. W. Beck of Vassar College while the statuette was in the workshop of J. Ternbach in New York.

Very little amber has been found in a Mediterranean context between the Tiryns hoard pieces and the eighth century BC. At the end of this century amber again became either available (the route having halted in Macedonia) or fashionable: 212 fragments were found in excavations on Rhodes, 46 on Ithica – including two small figures of animals and a pin head – and 54 at Perachora – including some intaglio seals (Strong, 1966).

In ancient Greece, amber was used extensively as an inlay with gold and ivory. Especially popular were the bronze and amber fibulae (pin brooches) worn on garments by both men of rank and by ladies. The blind poet Homer writes of amber several times in *The Odyssey*. What is of great interest is the fact that, according to the narrative, the resin is unusual, so this gives some idea as to the period of reintroduction:

'There came a man versed in craft to my father's house, with a golden chain hung here and there with amber beads. Now the maidens in the hall and my lady mother were handling the chain and gazing on it, and offering them their price.' (Book XV)

'For Antinous his henchman bare a 'broidered robe, great and very fair, wherein were golden brooches, twelve in all fitted with bent clasps. And the henchman straightway bare Eurymachus a golden chain of curious work, strung with amber beads shining like the sun.' (Book XVIII)

The Greek Legend for the origin of amber comes from this period and is told in full below:

Phaeton was the son of the God Apollo and the nephew of Diana the Huntress, but his mother was only a nymph, so he was destined for the life of a mortal.

As he grew he began to doubt his parentage, and his mother suggested that he should travel to the land where the sun rises, and ask his father to confirm his origins.

The palace of the sun stood raised on golden columns, encrusted with precious stones, and the ceilings were formed of milky-white ivory, whilst the doors were of beaten silver. Apollo was seated upon a throne, attended by the hours, the days, the months and the years. The four seasons were present 'Spring stood with her head crowned with flowers, and summer, with garment cast aside, and a garland formed of spears of ripened grain, and Autumn with his feet stained in grapejuice, and icy Winter with his hair stiffened with hoar frost.'

The youth was dazzled with such finery, but at last plucked up courage to approach the God. Apollo agreed immediately that Phaeton was his son and asked him to make a wish – an offer that was soon repented, for the youth asked to be allowed to drive the chariot of the sun across the sky, just for one day.

Apollo was horrified by the request, and told him to remember that he was only mortal, and not nearly strong enough for such a task. But Phaeton was stubborn, and Apollo looked on with foreboding as the lad took the reins, warning: 'The first part of the way is steep, and such as the horses even when fresh in the morning can hardly climb. The middle is high up in the heavens, whence, I myself can scarcely without alarm, look down and behold the earth and sea stretched beneath me. The last part of the road descends rapidly, and requires most careful driving. Tethys, who is waiting to receive me, often trembles for me lest I should fall headlong.'

However the wilful child did not listen to the warning, and set off on his long journey across the skies [*Figure 2.7*]. Almost at once the horses sensed that their load that day was lighter than usual, and the chariot carrying the sun began to sway between the signs in the sky. The Great and Little Bear were scorched, the wheels of the chariot were almost caught by the arms of the Scorpion and the jaws of the lion. The faster the horses pulled their load, the more frightened the youth became. The sun began to appear high in the heavens, then

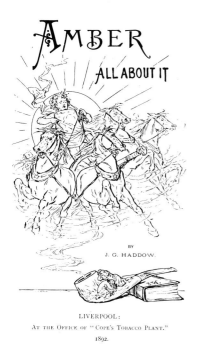

Figure 2.7 Title page from *Amber – All About It*, by J. G. Haddow, depicting the Greek Legend of Phaeton.

low beneath the surprised moon, close to the earth. It brushed past the centre of the globe, making the mountains catch fire and turning the people of Ethiopia black, whilst the waters dried up forming great deserts. The Nile in alarm fled and buried its source in this desert where it was safer.

Horrified, the Earth God called upon Jupiter to stop the child, but he was reluctant for Phaeton was the son of Apollo. However, Earth and Neptune reminded the gods that they had done much for mankind, so Jupiter sent a thunderbolt to kill Phaeton, and the youth fell like a shooting star from the skies, his hair on fire, into the river Eridanus.*

At length the nymphs of the river buried him, and his mother and sisters, the Heliades, came to weep by his grave. As they wept the Gods felt compassion for them, and that they might remain by the body for eternity, they were turned into poplar trees, and the tears that they wept were transformed to the golden gem – amber. (*Bulfinch's Mythology*, 1964 edition)

This legend, possibly dating back to the eighth century BC, was very popular in classical Greece and Rome. It may, however, have had a sinister counterpart, as a curious ritual death was once practised when a boy was chosen to be king, just for one day – the boy interrex – and he was then killed, usually by horses.

The fashion for amber dwindled in Greece after 600 BC but continued for another 200 years in the Greek colonies of the Italian peninsula and further afield.

Amber from the Italian peninsula abounds in the sixth and fifth centuries BC, occurring first among the Etruscan people who used it as inlays, beads for fibulae, scarabs and small-figure pendants. Because Etruria was the first part of the Italian peninsula to employ amber extensively, many other later Italian ambers are vaguely termed Etruscan when in fact they are from the southern states.

*Considered by some to be the river Po, this being a trading post for amber supplies at this period.

Most of the rich carvings associated with Italian ambers come from settlements like Picenum, Apulia, Calabria, Lucania, Campania and Latium.

From the latter group come a series of head pendants in two distinct styles. Whereas those with large almond eyes and hair depicted by a group of parallel lines appear all over the peninsula, a second more realistic style is restricted to what is now southern Italy (*Figure 2.8*). Common designs are fertility amulets in the form of rams' heads and cowrie shells, bulla bottle pendants, and animals both real and imaginary. (Aesop first published his book of animal fables in this period.)

The subject matter for major Italian amber carvings was of a devotional nature but, in this pre-Christian era, the figures depicted sometimes appear enigmatic to our eyes today. Many of the works depict Greek and Roman myths and legends.

Picenum is probably the most prolific area in Italy for finds of ancient amber. The carvings continue the strange oriental style so often found in Etruria, but the lion is a more dominant subject in place of the Etruscan monkey.

It is thought that although amber was traded from Trieste to Picenum, it was not worked locally. The finer pieces found in Picenum may therefore be imports. Among finds are a bulla with a Medusa head on one side and a series of little heads decorating the edge, a double lion arranged along a fibula, two groups of lions attacking a wild animal, and an outstanding carving (*Figure 2.9, part 1*) of a youth and a woman reclining on a couch (the legend of Pygmalion?).

Figure 2.8 Italic head pendants.

Strong (1966) differentiated two groups or styles in the more elaborate ambers carved in Italy in this period (*Figure 2.9, parts 1* and *2*). The towns of manufacture are not known but it seems probable that those of highest quality were worked in the south and then distributed. The influence of style seems to be allied to Campanian art of the same period.

The Bronze and Iron Ages, Central Europe: Hallstatt period

Whereas in the Bronze Age amber reached the south of Europe via the Elbe and the Rhine from Jutland, in the Iron Age a second route developed from the eastern Baltic area, by way of the Vistula. This latter route extended not just to the Mediterranean but also to the Black Sea.

The link between the Bronze and Iron Ages from the viewpoint of amber is the

(a)

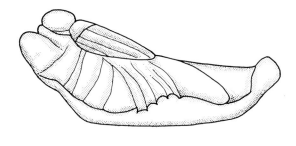

Figure 2.9 part 1 Italic carving of a
youth and woman reclining on a couch.
(a) front, (b) reverse. *Metropolitan
Museum of Art, New York.*

(b)

Hallstatt period, which takes its name from a cemetery near Salzburg, Austria in use
700 to 450 BC.

The area rose to importance from the production and trade of salt and copper, and
it became the centre of the major routes across Europe. Its importance in the history
of the use of amber results from the fact that the finds from this area include not only
imported amber goods but also others thought to be of local manufacture, which in
turn were distributed by river over a large area of south-east Europe.

The amber was used, somewhat crudely, in necklaces, fibulae, as pin heads and as
inlay. Over 659 amber beads have been discovered, and 26 more complex spacer
beads. The beads can be divided into two types: flattened, globular beads from the
middle Bronze Age, and truncated, biconical beads exclusive to the late Bronze Age.

Although some of the more exotic finds were probably imported – the bronze
fibulae threaded with amber segments were probably made in Italy – there are so
many necklaces and ornaments with the ratio of one or two spacers to a large number
of smaller beads, that it is thought that jewellery of this type was made locally.

Examples of this from the older phase include grave 343 (a spacer with four
perforations and about 130 beads), and grave 495 (a spacer with seven perforations
and 364 small biconical beads). From the younger phase are grave 377 (a spacer with
five perforations and 60 biconical beads) and grave 671 (a spacer with several

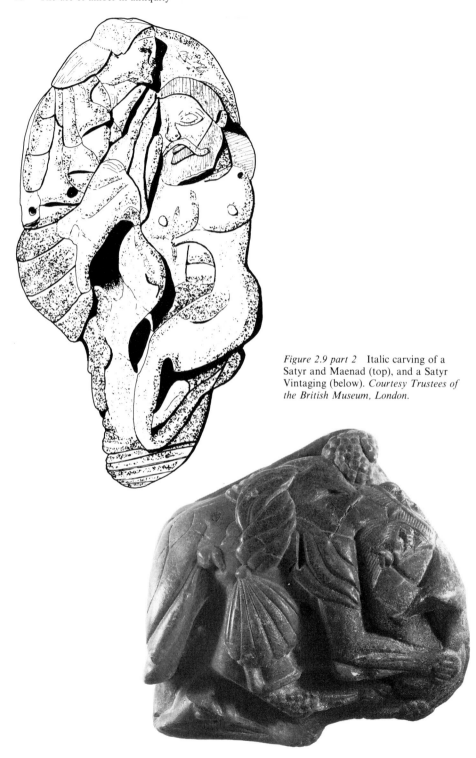

Figure 2.9 part 2   Italic carving of a Satyr and Maenad (top), and a Satyr Vintaging (below). *Courtesy Trustees of the British Museum, London.*

perforations and 77 beads). Not all the spacers are of amber; sometimes they are of horn or bone. Decoration, if any, is restricted to dotted circles.

Many of the Hallstatt finds are now in the Naturhistorisches Museum, Vienna, the National Museum in Budapest, and the British Museum, London.

Pelka (1920) illustrates a find from Bosnia (then in the Sarajevo Museum) where the metal fibula, as well as being decorated with amber nodules, has three chains of smaller beads hanging as pendants from the bar. A similar item is illustrated in Beck and Sprincz (1983) from Hallstatt and exhibited in the National Museum in Budapest. The latter has a spacer bead in addition to the three pendant chains.

Von Sacken, writing in the nineteenth century, reported that apart from the usual beads a diadem of eight rows of beads was found near the head of a male skeleton.

In Britain it must be remembered that the Iron Age continued until the occupation by the Romans. An outstanding find from this period is a large amber necklace from a female grave at Birdlip, Gloucestershire. This dates from AD 43, just prior to the Roman invasion.

Roman amber

Although Rome was founded in 753 BC, the use of amber is restricted to the period between the first century BC and the first century AD. Roman interest in the decorative arts was fostered initially by the constant stream of plundered treasure brought home from victorious campaigns – over 2000 statues alone from the Etruscan town of Veksuna. So much wealth was generated by this influx of antiquities that no taxes were levied on Roman citizens for many years.

The earliest objects of amber made by the Romans appear to be images of actors or grotesques. They are also found in other media such as terracotta. Various actors exist in the collection of the British Museum in London, and two – numbers 111 and 112 – are particularly interesting as they are taken from an identical design (*Figure 2.10*). The use of amber, always a talisman throughout history, may not be by chance for there are records at an earlier period of Etruscan actors being sent to Rome to placate the gods when there was a plague.

Three hoards of amber, amounting to 2750 kg, have been found between Osielsk

Figure 2.10 Two identical figures of Roman actors, showing mass production of limited themes.

and the mouth of the Adriatic. They date from the first century BC and show that amber was still being traded southwards from the Baltic, even if it was not reaching the Mediterranean.

Although the majority of later Roman ambers were made in Aquileia at the mouth of the Adriatic, only one actor statue has been found in this city. It is therefore thought that the actors were made in the south, nearer to Pompei or Nola.

One of the earliest 'Roman' literary allusions to amber comes from Virgil, who enjoyed patronage during the relatively calm reign of the Emperor Augustus.*

> 'Now let the wolf of himself fly from the sheep:
> the hard oaks bear golden apples,
> the alder with narcissus bloom,
> the tamarisks distil rich amber from their barks.' (Eclogue VIII)

Virgil also talks of light boots garnished with gold and amber.

From the same period survives Strabo's *Geography* – 17 volumes in Greek, which include descriptions of the recently entered Britannia and Germania – and part of Livy's 132-volume *Roman History*. There is a record of an amber portrait of Augustus at Olympia, but its present whereabouts are not known.

It is very likely that amber was only worked during certain periods of the two centuries under discussion. This would have been guided by whoever, as patron, ruled the Empire at the time. Tiberius, a thrifty, reserved man, detested public spectacle. Caligula and Claudius were steeped in family intrigue, and it is probably by chance that Nero found himself fostering an amber boom in the mid-first century AD.

Emperor Nero (AD 56–68) murdered his first wife in order to marry Poppaea Savina. This lady was presumably fair-haired, an unusual attribute among Mediterranean people, and in a poem the Emperor described her hair as 'succinum' or amber coloured. As happens today, the fashion was thus instantly created. Flaxen-haired slaves were unceremoniously shaved, wigs and false fringes were *de rigueur*, and amber itself became a favourite symbol of luxury.

The main centre of importation and manufacture was the city of Aquileia (*Figure 2.11*). Popular items were rings – very thickly worked with figures such as Venus or Cupid around the shank or, in later models, ladies with elaborate coiffeurs. Small toilet vessels were made, with lids carefully turned on a lathe to give perfect alignment. Tiny flasks (amphora) and mirror handles have also survived, but there is little evidence today of the larger vases which are said to have been made. (There is, however, a record of pieces of one such vase from the nineteenth-century inventory of the Museum at Rouen.)

The differences between Italic and Roman amber carvings are quite apparent. Whereas in the former the shape of the lump gave the eventual design to the piece, i.e. sculptured limbs curved around corners, sometimes giving rise to gross distortions, by the first century AD the design dictated the eventual shape of the object (*Figure 2.12*).

The Italic pieces are worked in low relief, and the graving tool was used only to outline the hairstyle and the features of the face. By Nero's reign the drill and the lathe

---

*Emperors of the Roman Empire: Augustus 31 BC to AD 14; Tiberius AD 14 to 37; Caligula AD 37 to 41; Claudius AD 41 to 54; Nero AD 54 to 68.

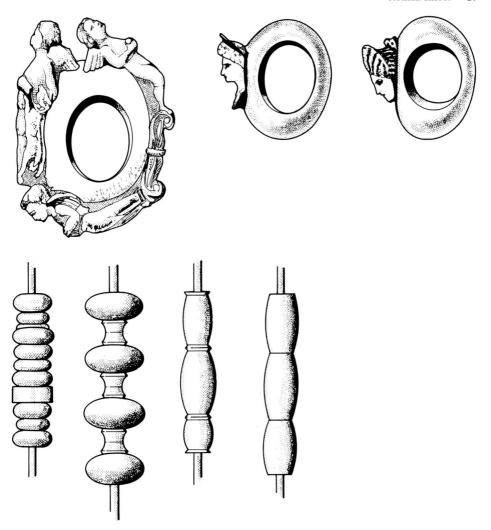

Figure 2.11 Ring designs and mirror handles (or sceptres) from the Roman town of Aquileia. (First century AD)

had been brought into use for amber carving, and this probably enabled the production of a larger number of items. The lathe was used not just for pots but also for amber discs – components of sceptres. The drill was also used for designating nostrils or pupils, or marking playing dice with their dot and ring motifs.

Fruit, cereals and animal figures were especially popular as New Year gifts, and this reinforces amber's continued link as a fertility amulet. The fall of the Roman population (as opposed to that of slaves or non-Romans) was a serious worry throughout the life of the Empire. Special tax relief and bonus systems were in force, and couples without children were barred from certain degrees of status. It is hardly surprising, therefore, that there are considerable numbers of phallic amulets and negro heads (the latter representing the fecundity of Africa) from the Roman period.

Figure 2.12 Satyr pot lid. (First century AD)

An account exists from Pliny of the great expedition to the north to collect amber at source, undertaken during the reign of Emperor Nero.

Julianus, manager of the gladiatorial exhibitions, wishing to curry favour with the Emperor, had one of the equestrian order sent north to obtain the amber.

In the *Natural History* (volume 37 of an encyclopaedic work and the only one to survive), Pliny the Elder relates:

'There still lives the Roman knight who was sent to procure amber by Julianus, superintendent of the gladitorial games given by Emperor Nero. This knight travelled over the markets and the shores of the country, and brought back such an immense quantity of amber that the nets intended to protect the podium from the wild beasts were studded with buttons of amber. Adorned likewise with amber were the arms, the biers, and the whole apparatus for one day. The largest piece the knight brought weighed thirteen pounds.'

Pliny recounts all the theories present in Greek and Roman literature about the origin of amber, but then concludes:

'It is certain that amber is produced in the islands north of the northern ocean that is called Glessum by the Germans, and that, for this reason, when Germanicus Caesar was commanding a fleet in those regions, the Romans gave the name of Glessaria to one of these islands ... Amber is formed by the pith (medulla or marrow) which flows from trees of the pine species, as a gum flows from cherry-trees and resin from pines. It is, first of all a liquid which bursts forth in abundance; then it is congealed by the cold, or by the heat, or by the sea, when the great tides rise and sweep it from the islands. At all events, it is thrown on to the coasts, in so light a form, that it seems to be suspended in the water, and does not sink to the bottom. Our ancestors, thinking that it was the sap (saccus) of a tree, called it on that account, succinum. The proof that amber is the product of a species of pine, is that when rubbed it exhales an odour like that of the pine, and that when set on fire it burns after a fashion, with the scent of a resinous torch. It is conveyed by the Germans into Pannonia (Hungary) chiefly; thence the Veneti (Venetians), whom the Greeks call Heniti, who are in immediate proximity to Pannonia, and who live round the Adriatic Sea, have brought it into vogue.

There are many kinds of amber; the white is that which has the sweetest scent; but neither the white nor the wax-coloured is worth much. The deep yellow (fulvus, tawny, fallow) is the most esteemed. Though the transparency of the deep yellow amber is a recommendation, intense brilliancy is objectionable. To please there must be present, not fire but the resemblance of fire. The amber most in request is Falernian, so called because it has the colour of Falernian wine. It is transparent, and has a softened splendour. Certain kinds attract by a tender shade, like the tint of boiled honey; but it ought to be known that any colour can be given to amber that is thought fit. A particular dye can be given to it by means of kid fat, or of the anchusa root; it can even be made to take a purple tinge . . . Bits of amber in oil burn with a brighter and more enduring flame than wicks of flax tow . . . Amber can be efficiently and extensively employed in imitating translucid precious stones, especially amethysts; for as we have said, it can be tinged to every colour.'

The second great text covering amber from the Roman period is the volume entitled *Germania*, written by Tacitus in AD 98. Tacitus was Roman Governor of Germany between 89 and 93, so he had a unique opportunity of reporting directly from northern Europe:

'Turning to the right shore of the Suebian sea, we find it washing the territories of the Aestii, who have the religion and general customs of the Suebi, but a language approximating to the British. They worship the Mother of Gods. They wear, as emblem of this cult, the masks of boars, which stand them in stead of armour or human protection and ensure safety of the worshipper even among his enemies. They seldom use weapons of iron, but cudgels often. They cultivate grain and other crops with a patience quite unusual among lazy Germans. Nor do they omit to ransack the sea; they are the only people to collect the amber – glaesum is their own word for it – in the shallows or even on the beach. Like true Barbarians, they have never asked or discovered what it is or how it is produced. For a long time, indeed, it lay unheeded like any other jetsam, until Roman luxury made its reputation.

They gather it crude, pass it on unworked and are astounded at the price it fetches. Amber however, is certainly a gum of trees, as you may see from the fact that creeping and even winged creatures are often seen shining in it. They got caught in the sticky liquid and were imprisoned as it hardened. I imagine in the islands and lands of the west, just as in the secret chambers of the east, where the trees sweat frankincense and balm, there must be woods and groves of unusual fertility. There gums, drawn out by the rays of their near neighbour, the sun, flow in liquid state into the sea and are finally washed by violent storms on to the shores opposite. If you care to test the properties of amber by applying fire to it, you will find that it lights like a torch and gives off a thick and heavily scented flame; then it cools to a sticky solid like pitch or resin. Continuous with the Suiones are the nation of the Sitones. They resemble them in all respects but one – woman is the ruling sex. That is the measure of their decline.'

The movement of the Goths across Europe seems to have disrupted the amber trade route to the Mediterranean. The Goths had reached as far as the south of the Black Sea in AD 151 and attempted to attack Aquileia itself in the 170s. After AD 200, carvings in amber do not appear in southern contexts but they are found scattered in the far dominions of the Empire for another 200 years, perhaps handed-down heirlooms of a greater age.

The Goths did not prevent amber trade completely, for while amber becomes rare in Mediterranean lands at this period, there is a correspondingly large increase of its incidence in Bohemian graves in central Europe. It is often forgotten that the Goths originated from the island of Scandza or Gotland, and settled early on in their travels around the mouth of the Vistula. Thus amber would be familiar to these peoples.

Bibliography

BECK, C. W and BOCQUET, A., *Découverte à Charavines (Isere) d'Ambre Neolithique Provenant de la Mer Baltique*, Academie des Inscriptions et Belles Lettres, Paris (1982)

BECK, C. W. and SPRINCZ, E., 'The origin of amber found at Hallstatt', *Acta Archaeologicia Academiae Scientiarum Hungaricae*, **35** (1983)

BULFINCH, T. (1796–1867), *Bulfinch's Mythology*, reprinted by Hamlyn, London (1964)

CURWEN, E. and CURWEN, E.C., *The Hove Tumulus*, Brighton and Hove Archaeologist Club (1924)

HARDING, A. and HUGHES-BROCK, H., *Amber in the Mycenaean World*, 14th Annual Meeting of British School of Archaeology at Athens (1974)

JENSEN, J., *Nordens Guld*, Gyldendalske Boghandel, Nordisk Forlag, Copenhagen (1982)

TRATMAN, E.K., 'Amber from paleolithic deposits: Goughs Cave', *Proc. Brist. Spelaeo. Soc.*, **6,** No. 3 (1950)

KING, C. W., *Antique Gems: Their Origin, Uses and Value* (1860)

LUCAS, A. and HARRIS, J. R., 'Ancient Egyptian materials and industries', quoted by Harding and Hughes-Brock (*see* above)

PELKA, O., *Bernstein*, Richard Carl Schmidt, Berlin (1920)

STRONG D. E., *Catalogue of the Carved Amber in the Department of Greek and Roman Antiquities*, British Museum, London (1966)

VON SACKEN, Das Grabfeld von Hallstatt. (78); in: Denny Papers, Mineralogy Library, British Museum of Natural History, London

Chapter 3

Unsettled Europe

The first millennium after Christ is marked by a movement of peoples across Europe, with frequent warfare, particularly from about AD 300 to 800.

However, the internationalizing influence of the Roman Empire cannot be overstated. Soldiers signed up for a quarter century in return for Roman citizenship, and during this period they saw service at all corners of the Empire. Thus there are gravestones in rural Gloucestershire to soldiers from what today are Albania and Yugoslavia. This movement of peoples was at all levels. The Emperor himself, Septimus Severus, ended his days in the early third century at Eburacum (York). He was born in Libya, and his wife in Syria.

The result of all this displacement with regard to amber is that although the resin seems to have lost popularity in Rome after the first century AD, ambers worked in a classical style are still found spasmodically in the Empire and beyond. It is thought that these finds are souvenirs or heirlooms rather than the result of new trade. Examples of this can be found in the two cemeteries at the Butt Road site in Colchester, Essex generally dated to third and early fourth centuries AD. From period 1 comes an amber head with the hair piled into a tiered coiffeur (*Figure 3.1*). The head, measuring 1.9 cm, was found with what possibly had been a chain purse, and from its negroid characteristics and grotesque form could even have been used as

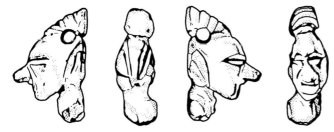

Figure 3.1 Amber head pendant or clasp showing hair piled high into an elaborate coiffeur, and negroid features. Found at Colchester, England, third century AD cemetery, but the amber is an earlier import.

the catch. Other amulets were found with the amber head: a pierced dog's canine, a copper alloy horned phallus, an as of Hadrian, the coin enclosed in a frame of silver, a copper alloy bell and clapper, and two pierced coins. The objects have holes drilled for suspension, but these are too small to be linked to the copper alloy chains. All were found in the remains of an iron pan (Crummy, 1980).

An amber bottle-shaped pendant has been found in the Fordington Hill cemetery, Dorchester, with a necklace of beads of glass, bone and pearls (blister and seed). This is dated c.300 by a coin of Constantine associated with a nearby grave. Amber beads have also been found in these late Roman graves but never more than singly or in pairs, indicating the amuletic properties of amber rather than its availability as a regular form of jewellery.

Anglo-Saxon Germanic tribes were brought in to defend the province in the fourth century, but Rome itself fell to the Goths in 410, and by that time the last Roman garrison had left Britain.

As would be expected from events previously covered, the relative absence of amber within the Roman Empire was counterbalanced by the appearance of amber beyond the Empire in quantity. The third and fourth centuries are marked by large-scale Baltic exportation of simple beads in association with others of glass, rock crystal and cornelian. A special form of amber bead, unique to the fourth century, was marketed from the island of Bornholm over a wide area (Jensen, 1982).

A grave from the Iron Age of about AD 400 was found in exceptionally good condition at Lille Bjerggard, Denmark in 1973. The entire excavation was removed by lorry to Aalborg Museum, and shows the skeleton of a woman of 40 years and of above average height. The dead woman lay on her side and slight traces remained of her garment (*Figure 3.2*). As decoration she wore three fibulae (one at each shoulder and one at the waist) and on her chest a rope of about 150 beads, mostly amber. Other

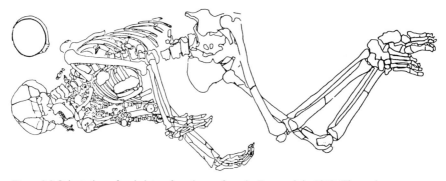

Figure 3.2 Orientation of a skeleton found on a farm in Denmark in 1973. The amber was sewn onto the costume, and the three fibulae allow the date of burial to be put at around AD 400. *Aalborg Museum.*

beads formed a choker around her neck. It is interesting that the rope of beads apparently was attached to the front of the dress rather than around the neck (*Figure 3.3*). From similar burials it is likely that the material of the dress had a checked pattern.

A legacy from the Roman Empire, long after its demise, are sets of amber playing

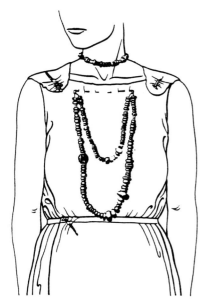

Figure 3.3 Probable method of using the fibulae and jewellery found on the skeleton at Lille Bjerggard. Aalborg Museum.

Figure 3.4 Amber playing pieces found in Northern Europe, a legacy of the Roman Empire.

pieces (the gamesboards were made of wood) from the Roman game ludus latrunculorum (*Figure 3.4*). These playing pieces have been found in locations outside the boundary of the Empire, such as Vimose on the island of Fyn.

Finds of amber disappear locally within Denmark between AD 400 and 700 (Jensen, 1982) but are found extensively, especially in the mid to late sixth century, in Anglo-Saxon cemeteries. Amber beads have so far been found in about 150 early Anglo-Saxon cemeteries (Meaney, 1981). In the main restricted to southern and eastern England, the beads are usually of flattish discoidal shape and appear roughly finished when compared to spacer plates, for example, of an earlier period. At the peak of its popularity the amber is found in long strings in the pagan graves, whereas at other times it is restricted to single finds, often in the graves of children. As amber is also associated with the burial of warriors – often an 'amber sword-bead' is found in such burials – the use of amber was probably associated with religion or superstition rather than beauty. This link between the use of amber and some pagan superstition is strengthened by the knowledge that, on the continent at least, Christian religious leaders preached against its usage. Christianity had been reintroduced to Kent by St. Augustine in the sixth century, but amber is very seldom found in Christian graves.

'Among the remains of heathen superstition enumerated by St. Eloi in the early 7th century – amber necklaces as a charm for women and their infants, and as a relief for children.' (Jones, 1880)

Amber was frequently used *en cabochon* with the magnificent silver Celtic brooches of northern Scotland, but the author has yet to see these included in general books about amber. These pins with brooch heads or penannular brooches date from the eighth and ninth centuries AD and are associated with the early migrations of Norse people. The most famous such brooch was found at Hunterston, Ayrshire in 1821. Made of silver gilt, it has animals in gold wire and granulation on the front, and on the back spiral and interlaced designs. The front is set with amber cabochons and the back also has a later Viking runic tenth-century inscription.

Other such brooches have been found, for example, at Rogart, Dunipace, Achavrole, and on the island of Iona. Two such brooches are illustrated (*Figures 3.5* and *3.6*). These brooches remained popular for a long period. One from Westness, on the island of Orkney, was found in an unusually rich ninth-century grave dating from the earliest Nordic inhabitants of the area. What makes this find unusual is that the brooch was already at least a century old when buried.

Figure 3.5 Penannular brooch of silver overlaid with gold, and set with amber. Rogart, Scotland. Eighth/ninth century AD.

The Norse people also brought with them a fine workmanship for amber beads; one find, from Dun an Iardhard on the Island of Skye, is of a necklace of 59 very finely graduated amber beads.

Schleswig can claim to be the first small town in Viking Europe, being established at around AD 700. Its difference from previous agglomerations was the presence of workshops where crafts were carried out in a specialized, ordered fashion. An amber workshop was one of several in the town, the others being workshops for gold, bronze, etc. The objects produced were smooth beads, wedge-shaped pendants and rings, and the method was apparently one of trial and error, for when similar items from Jorvic (York, England) are looked at in depth (*Figure* 3.7) one sees that the amber was scraped using too much force and the surface was pitted due to excess pressure. A third find of Viking amber is in Dublin.

Figure 3.6 (a) and (b). Brooch of silver gilt, with amber settings. Hunterston, Scotland. Eighth/ ninth century AD.

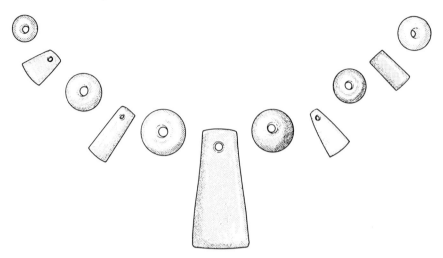

Figure 3.7 Tenth century amber jewellery from the Viking period of Jorvic (York).

Whereas one would expect this to be a period of popularity for amber, the use of this resin by Vikings in Scandinavia is also extremely rare.

There are a few amber axes, associated with the worship of Thor; examples are to be found at Bjorko, Sweden and the Lindholm Hills site in North Jutland, Denmark.

Other items fall into the category of 'sundries'; two enigmatic faces have been found on beaches in Denmark, and a third dated to around AD 800. Identical playing pieces of curled hounds occur (*Figure 3.8*), usually in Norway, and two curious bearded games-pieces – one from Roholte on Zealand and one from Schleswig (*Figure 3.9*).

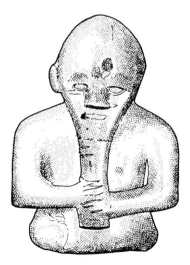

Figure 3.8 Norwegian games piece in the shape of a curled hound.

Figure 3.9 Games piece of human form.

Little is known of amber in Norman times, or indeed in Europe of the tenth and eleventh centuries; however, ironically, the rising power of the Christian church eventually brought the resin into demand again, as a source material for rosaries.

Bibliography

CHAMPION, T., GAMBLE, C., SHENNAN, S. and WHITTLE, A., *Prehistoric Europe*, Academic Press, London (1984)

CRUMMY, N., *The Roman Small Finds from Excavations in Colchester 1971–79*, Colchester Archaeological Report No. 2 (1980)

JENSEN, J., *Nordens Guld*, Gyldendalskc Boghandel, Nordisk Forlay, Copenhagen (1982)

JONES, W., 'Credulities past and present', p. 170 (1880); in: Denny Papers, Mineralogy Library, British Museum (Natural History), London

MEANEY, A. L., 'Amber: Saxon amulets and curing stones', *BAR British Series*, **96** (1981)

Chapter 4

European Renaissance amber

Amber flourished during the Renaissance largely due to royal patronage, and the gemmologist attached to a fine arts house should be able to ascribe certain styles of amber carving to certain centuries within this period.

Although the movement reached its zenith during the seventeenth century, its roots can be traced back to the thirteenth century when the Teutonic Order of Knights rose to importance in the politics of northern Europe.

The Teutonic Order had been founded to fight in the Crusades and returned to Europe in 1211. As the Order was an excellent mercenary force, its aid was requested to subdue rebellious Prussians along the Baltic coast, and this was undertaken with such verve that eventually the entire territory was conquered. In 1309 the Grand Master of the Order, Siegfried von Feuchtwangen, marked this by moving their headquarters from Venice to Marienburg (Malbork).

Initially, the value of the amber within their domains does not seem to have been realized by the Knights. In 1257, the Bishop of Samland was granted the fishing rights on the coast of Samland, the Danzig fishermen likewise in 1312, and the monastery of Oliva in 1340. What the Knights did impose, however, was a strict code of discipline and, although the local people were allowed to collect the amber, they were not allowed to keep it or work it within the territory of the Order. This simple but far-reaching rule that all amber had to be exported to specific warehouses or guilds initially far away from the Baltic, has left us with the unusual position that for many centuries there was no cottage industry for amber carving at source.

Until the late sixteenth century most of the amber was turned into paternoster beads or vessels. The main centres of production were Bruges (established by 1302) and Lübeck (established by 1360). Not many examples of these early rosaries survive, but fourteenth-century rosary beads in various stages of manufacture have been excavated from the site of Baynard's Castle in London. It is also thought that amber working took place at Weismar but, again, there is no written evidence to support this claim.

The fourteenth century is still rather a mystery with regard to amber carving. We know of the two Guilds of Paternoster Makers in Bruges and Lübeck but have little of substance to demonstrate their work. On the other hand, we have inventories from the royal houses of France and Burgundy covering much more complex objects but no reference as to where they were made. In 1361, the French king appropriated the Duchy of Burgundy and made it over to his son Philip the Bold. The latter married the heiress of Flanders and Antwerp and thereby enlarged the realm. This alliance may be the source.

1379: A relief in amber of the Holy Family, with the Three Kings and St. Anastasius.
       An amber Madonna with a gold coronet garnished with pearls.
1389: A figure of St. Margaret and the dragon mounted in silver gilt.
       Three knives with handles of amber.

Cutlery handles in amber were made throughout the Renaissance. The fork was introduced at the French court in the fourteenth century but was slow to be taken up elsewhere.

The whereabouts of the aforementioned items are not known but two objects, very similar to each other, have survived. These are small amber reliefs of the head of Christ, in silver gilt and enamel frames. One example is in Munich (Bayerisches National Museum) and is dated 1380, while the other is part of the Wallace Collection in London and is set in a mid-fifteenth century frame (*Figure 4.1*).

Figure 4.1 Amber relief of the head of Christ (fourteenth/fifteenth century) set in a silver gilt and enamel frame. *The Wallace Collection, London.*

The fifteenth century

The fifteenth century marks the rise of Poland and the first defeats for the Teutonic Order, who had ruled from east Prussia to Estonia for nearly a century and a half. By 1430 the Polish Empire reached from the Baltic to the Black Sea, but Danzig did not fall until 1466.

Pomerania also rose to brief importance as Erik of Pomerania inherited Denmark, Sweden and Norway from his great-aunt Queen Margaret. We know that the Guild of Stolp in Pomerania was founded in the fifteenth century, but only by reference to the fact that the citizens of nearby Danzig were initially discouraged by the authorities from establishing their own guild because of the existence of Stolp. The Danzig amber guild was eventually established in 1477.

The production of amber rosaries continued. Oil paintings of the period frequently depict such paternosters as part of the composition. The Dutch brothers Van Eyck introduced oil painting to Europe, and Jan Van Eyck wrote a treatise on the preparation of varnish. One of the most famous of his works, the Arnolfini Marriage (National Gallery, London), appears to show an amber rosary on the rear wall. A painting where such an amber rosary plays an even more central role is the fifteenth-century Madonna and Child from Liptonadasd (Hungarian National Gallery, Budapest).

Records exist of amber rosaries in Britain at this time, and the substance was obviously of considerable value because often only one or two beads were given as legacies.

1463:   John Baret to the Abbot of Bury St. Edmunds: his 'bedys of white amber with the ring of silver and ovir gilt longyng there to' (a gilt cross).
         A 'peyre' of amber beads to each of seven legatees, as well as to 'eche yoman of my household'.
1504:   Anne Barrett. To the Lord Abbot of Bury St. Edmunds: 'grete bedys of whyght ambyr' (Williamson, 1932).

The production of more sizeable articles also continued. European inventories of ambers include:

1412:   Duc de Berry. A relief of the Madonna, mounted on wood.
1416:   Duc de Berry. Madonna with a gold crown under a baldacchino.
1418:   Treasury of the Louvre. Amber crucifix.
1483:   Charlotte of Savoy. A small relief of Christ's Head.
1514:   Charlotte d'Albret. A dozen amber paternosters (Gay, 1887).

Two items which illustrate this period are a statue of a seated Madonna from Lüneburg, now in the Kestner Museum, Hannover, and a pair of cruets for the Mass, probably made in Lübeck or Bruges, and now in the Victoria and Albert Museum, London.

The sixteenth century

The sixteenth century is rent by the religious split caused by the Reformation. Martin Luther posted his 95 theses against the sale of indulgences on the church door at Wittenburg in 1517, and only eight years later Albrecht of Hohenzollern, Grand Master of the Order of Teutonic Knights, declared himself a Lutheran. At the same time he also declared himself Duke of Prussia, and set about increasing the wealth of his court in Königsberg (Kaliningrad).

In 1533, the duke handed over the marketing of amber to an agent, Paul Jaski, who, although from Danzig, appears to have promoted the sale of amber all over northern Europe – Königsberg, Augsburg, Breslau, Lübeck, Antwerp, etc. – with the exception of his home town. Jaski did sell amber to the Danzig Guild but the relationship was not a harmonious one.

The sixteenth century saw the foundation of other guilds – Koslin and Kolberg in Pomerania, and Elbing – but it was the city of Königsberg, with its history of goldsmithing and court patronage, that rose to the fore. The threat from Königsberg, even though it had no guild at this time, was such that in the mid-1580s a Union of Amber Guilds was formed between Kolberg, Stolp, Danzig and Elbing, with Danzig as the central base. But the tide of Lutheranism in northern Europe meant that there was less sales potential for rosaries or religious objects. Königsberg was Lutheran and the court patronage produced secular objects for the first time, mostly covered vessels. These covered vessels stand on slim stems with round amber bases, and are decorated with round 'buttons' of amber, similar to sixteenth-century silverwork from Antwerp.

As the Jaski family had strong connections with Antwerp, these merchants may have traded more than amber in the Baltic region. They retained the position of virtual sole agent from the mid-sixteenth to the mid-seventeenth century, but throughout this period their control is marked by squabbling between producers and manufacturers. In 1580, gallows were erected along the coast to deter the pocketing of amber, so the lot of the local inhabitants was still an unhappy one.

The covered vessels, usually made in Königsberg, can today be found in various museums. Apart from the roundels or 'buttons' previously alluded to, they were also decorated with metalwork, white osseous amber or meerschaum. Examples include: a covered vessel of 1560, made in Lübeck (Lübeck Museum für Kunst und Kulturgeschichte); a covered vessel of 1590 enclosing the shield of Sigismund III Vasa, King of Poland, made in Königsberg and now in Munich (Schatzkammer der Residenz); and two similar covered goblets, one in Munich and the other in Kassel (Staatliche Kunstsammlungen). All are illustrated in Reineking von Bock.

One of the first pieces, or sets of pieces, which can be dated with certainty is a group of 18 silver gilt and amber plates, made in Königsberg by master amber craftsman Stentzel Schmidt and goldsmith Andreas Knieffel. The plates were made for Georg Friedrich von Ansbach, Regent of Prussia, and each is complete with coats of arms on the front and the relevant country such as Schleswig or Denmark on the reverse (*Figure 4.2*).

Meanwhile, in those countries not affected by the Reformation, amber rosaries and religious figures were still in demand (*Figure 4.3*). In the Museo degli Argenti, Florence a magnificent collection of amber objects collected, from the sixteenth

Figure 4.2 One of a group of 18 silver gilt and amber plates
(sixteenth century) made in Konigsberg for the Regent of Prussia.
The Rosenberg Palace, Denmark.

Figure 4.3 (a) Front and (b) back of a religious carving showing the Virgin and Child, and Christ as a
man. The piece shows a curious mixture of styles.

century onwards, includes three amber rosaries, one already recorded in the gallery in 1589. There are also five amber statues of the Madonna and Child, with faces and hands in white amber, all recorded as sixteenth-century work.

The first books since the fall of the Roman Empire which covered amber in any depth appeared in the sixteenth century. This was a period of great expansion. The Jaski family were opening up markets as far away as Turkey and India, and apparently in the mid-sixteenth century Armenians travelled to Königsberg and bartered silk carpets for raw amber. Books which have survived include:

Agricola, G., *De Natura Fossilium* (1546). This contains the earliest account of obtaining succinic acid from amber.
Aurifaber, A., *Succini Historia*, Königsberg (1551)
Gobel, S., *History und eigendlichter bericht von herkommen Ursprung und vielfeltigen Branch des Bernsteins neben andern saubern Berkchkhartzen so der Gattung ... aus guten grundt der Philosphy.* (1556)

The seventeenth century

Late sixteenth-century and early seventeenth-century ambers show a strong continuity, so a division at 1600 is not a natural one. Königsberg continues as the central point for the finest work, with a concentration on gamesboards and items for Kunstkammer collections.

The first important date is 1611 when John Sigismund, Elector of Brandenburg, married Anna, heir to the Duchy of Prussia. The Elector later assimilated Prussia into Brandenburg and in 1618 moved the court totally to Berlin. From this date the Brandenburgs commissioned works from Danzig rather than Königsberg.

In 1630, Christian IV of Denmark landed in Pomerania and compelled the Elector of Brandenburg to enter into an alliance. In 1648, Pomerania became Swedish as part of the final settlement of the Thirty Years War. These events may have had an influence on the collections later made in Copenhagen and Uppsala.

Gamesboards

The late sixteenth and early seventeenth centuries are marked by the production of superb gamesboards in Königsberg. These boards, usually mounted on oak, carry chess and sometimes nine men's morris on the outer surface, and open to reveal backgammon in the interior.

Wooden gamesboards survive from an early period, where the playing pieces are of amber, but one of the first boards itself to be faced with amber is dated 1594 and is to be seen at Kassel Staatliche Kunstsammlungen. This board is of great importance as it heralds a new form of decoration for amber objects.

Another early gamesboard at Kassel is dated 1580–1590 but the chessboard is decorated with amber and white amber reliefs. The surrounds to these reliefs and other parts of the board are in painted foilwork. A key to this board is its block ivory and amber design on the outer edges. This composition is the same as that used on cutlery handles and flatware in Königsberg between 1588 and the early seventeenth century (*Figure 4.4*).

Up until this period amber had been used in a solid form, sometimes worked on a lathe, and decoration had been in the form of applied portrait busts in white amber or meerschaum, or metalwork supports. Often these portrait busts were covered-in with a thin plaque of clear amber and although today, due to atmospheric weathering, this masks the interior, when originally constructed the plaque acted as a virtually colourless window.

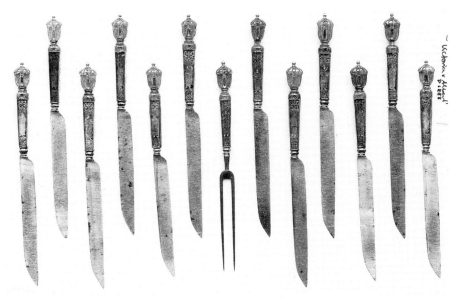

Figure 4.4 Cutlery set made in Konigsberg – sixteenth/seventeenth century. *Victoria and Albert Museum, London.*

The gamesboard in Kassel demonstrates this technique on the nine men's morris board, but the chessboard is made up of squares of osseous mottled amber and clear squares where the plaques protect a series of very fine engravings on metal foil. This type of work is called *eglomisé** but the term may cause confusion to the gemmologist, who is familiar with it in a far stricter setting.

Another example of this work is in the Victoria and Albert Museum, London, where what originally were the squares of a chessboard have been later transferred on to boxwood cores as bases for nineteenth-century groups. In neither the example in

*From the French eighteenth-century writer, artist and art dealer Jean-Baptiste Glomy. Although associated with glassware, it is also found on Spanish jewellery, especially reliquaries, of the sixteenth and seventeenth centuries.

To use the word *eglomisé*, from *verre églomise*, the amber itself should have been painted, and then the design etched away, whereas in fact it is far more usual for the foil behind the amber to have been painted, and this layer etched to expose the reflective metallic backing.

Kassel nor London do the engravings appear to have been made specially for the chessboards. It is more likely that, as in later periods with regard to amber-engraved decoration, the designs came from a copy book. This is particularly apparent as the portrait busts appear juxtaposed in various sizes of scale.

The engraved designs are in the main of cavaliers, or bearded men with stiff ruffs and a variety of hats. The London examples also depict women and animals, while the Kassal chessboard includes a king and two coats of arms. The fact that the morris board is actually dated 1594 as part of the decoration makes this piece of fundamental importance.

Any works of amber which can be dated are vital, as by this means similar objects can be categorized. A gamesboard (*Figure 4.5*) in the Victoria and Albert Museum, London, bears the inscription (in old German): 'Whoever wants to play this boardgame must have plenty of numbers; in 1620 God gives more in one day than the whole kingdom has. When I had plenty to give I got along with everyone; now that I no longer have, no one wishes me goodday. Good luck and glass; how soon they break!' This board has ivory strips, decorated with an inscribed pattern darkened with ink. A board in the Boston Fine Arts Museum also has this form of ivory banding. Both boards have coloured foil motifs and pierced white amber reliefs under clear amber plaques. The Boston board also has eight ivory plaques which are engraved in a similar manner to the ivory banding. The plaques show a huntsman, game birds and game animals. It is important to remark that these ivory panels are engraved, not pierced reliefs.

Figure 4.5 German gamesboard, dated 1620. *Victoria and Albert Museum, London.*

A magnificent gamesboard was sold in 1979 at the Mentmore auction, and has now been restored by the Bayerisches Nationalmuseum in Munich. This board has metal mounts bearing the mark of Andreas Meyer, who worked in Königsberg between 1598 and 1647. A second gamesboard, of which only the backgammon section remains, is of such similar style that it would be natural to assume they both came from the same workshop. This board is in the Victoria and Albert Museum, London.

There are other gamesboards in collections both public and private but they are usually also of late sixteenth or early seventeenth-century workmanship, with some exceptions. One is another gamesboard in the Boston Fine Arts Museum, complete with 32 chessmen (the gamespieces have been lost from most sets). The chessboard is with mottos in French under the clear sections set on round burn feet with a raised surround.

The Boston Fine Arts Museum also has 16 drafts pieces, said to go with the seventeenth-century gamesboard. Eight of the pieces are of cloudy amber and eight of clear amber. Each has a small ivory carved disc at the centre. In the same collection is a nineteenth-century set of chessmen made in Vienna for the Paris Exposition of 1879.

Michael Redlin was working in Danzig in 1688 and left designs for gamesboards, illustrated in *Die Meister der Bernstein-Kunst* by Otto Pelka. Two eighteenth-century gamesboards by Lorenz Spengler are in the collection of the Rosenborg Palace, Copenhagen.

Although amber caskets may originally have been made as retainers for games-pieces, their use continued over a large part of the Renaissance so they are dealt with in a later section.

The Master craftsman through this period was Georg Schreiber, known to be active in Königsberg between 1617 and 1643. The fact that Schreiber should be operating from the city that the Prussian court had just left is rather puzzling. Equally so is that only four items are known which bear his signature, and these are prior to the court's departure.

(1) A casket once in Königsberg. Signed and dated 1615 (Aschengreen Piacenti 1966).
(2) A tankard (1617), in Darmstadt Silberkammer. Inscribed: 'Georgius Scriba Borussus Civis et incola Regiomonti Borussorum hoc fecit' (illustrated in Pelka, 1920: Figure 66).
(3) A casket, Weimar Museum für Kunst und Kunstgewerbe. Signed but not dated (illustrated in Pelka, 1920: Figure 50).
(4) An altar, Museo degli Argenti, Florence. Dated 1618 on one plaque, and inscribed as the Darmstadt tankard with the date 1619 on another (Aschengreen Piacenti, 1966).

Other caskets, vessels, tankards and even candlesticks are attributed to Schreiber or his school but none of these bears any inscription. Most of these works were for Kunstkammer collections,* and although they cannot be dated they do fall into several decorative phases. As the object of greatest production was the lidded tankard, the emphasis in the following examples is placed on these 'Deckelhumpen'.

All the following Kunstkammer ambers have clear amber panels, carved in low relief. The designs on these panels extend 'busily' all over the exposed surface, and

---

*These cabinets of curiosities contained highly worked objects of ivory, amber or metal, often purely decorative, and these were exhibited with exotic birds, feathers and trophies of natural history.

illustrate secular subjects or are purely decorative. Although usually ascribed to the school of Georg Schreiber they must have been made at several centres. They all date from the early to mid-seventeenth century.

(1) Ambers that are glued and have little or no metalwork support. Clear amber only used (*Figure 4.6*):
  (a) low tankard, Leningrad. Hermitage (Staatliche Eremitage);
  (b) low tankard, Gotha Museum, East Germany;
  (c) tankard, British Museum, London;
  (d) Schraubflasche, Hessisches Landesmuseum, Darmstadt.

Figure 4.6 Seventeenth century tankard. *British Museum, London.*

(2) Ambers with little or no metal support but with cloudy amber bands. These bands are not carved:
  (a) tankard, Metropolitan Museum of Art, New York (metal mounts by Andreas Meyer, 1606–1647);
  (b) casket, Schatzkammer der Residenz, Munich;
  (c) two caskets, Staatliche Kunstsammlungen, Kassel.
(3) Amber with metal support and cloudy amber bands. These bands are perforated:
  (a) tankard, Metropolitan Museum of Art, New York (perforated with diamonds and cartouches of clear amber exposing design within);
  (b) tankard, Hessisches Landesmuseum, Darmstadt (very ornate amber and metalwork). Unique?

(4) As (3) with the addition of a wide band of metal on the upper rim of the vessel. This band gloriously enamelled with flowers and foliage:
   (a) tankard, Schatzkammer der Residenz, Munich;
   (b) tankard, Kunsthistorisches Museum, Vienna;
   (c) pitcher, Grünes Gewölbe, Dresden.
(5) A large group of ambers with plain, wide metal-lip supports and clear amber panels:
   (a) tankard, Museo degli Argenti, Florence;
   (b) two tankards, Schatzkammer der Residenz; Munich (c.1640–1650);
   (c) two tankards, British Museum, London (one dated 1659);
   (d) two-handled cup, Victoria and Albert Museum, London.

Many smaller items were worked for Kunstkammer collections: goblets, cups, screw-topped flasks and pieces of purely ornamental character. This is not a book for such detail and readers are advised to study the more specialist publications.

As always, there are some exceptional pieces of this period that do not fit into general categories. In Munich (Bayerisches Nationalmuseum) there is a carving of a wantonly posed nymph and a putti. This is engraved 'F de Q/1625' (François de Quesnoy). The freshness of this piece is exhilarating and this same quality is exhibited in a similar-sized piece of a crouching lion (*Figure 4.7*) in London (Victoria and Albert Museum). In Florence (Museo degli Argenti) there is an amber fountain dated to 1610, but elements of this piece suggest that it may be of a later date and it will be discussed in another section.

The 1640s saw big changes in the amber world. Frederick William of Brandenburg and East Prussia came to power and reigned as the Great Elector until 1688. His first task was to barter back the lease for the amber rights from the Jaski family. The Königsberg Amber Guild was formed, perhaps out of desperation, with only two members, one being the aged Georg Schreiber. But the guild did succeed, for although Schreiber ends his connection in 1643, in this year other names are registered for the first time: Schnipperling, Damcke, Kohn and Lemke. The guild did not finally close until the nineteenth century, but from its somewhat late inception it faced problems of working in an age when the court amber carvers were rising to prominence, these men not being guild members.

The Königsberg Guild was faced with a more immediate problem in the rise to premier status in the amber league of the city of Danzig, only 100 miles to the west. This mid-seventeenth century flowering seems to have been due to a combination of patronage by the Great Elector and the fact that the Jaski family had at last been relieved of their stranglehold on the market. The Great Elector had moved to Königsberg during the Thirty Years War for protection, but this ended with the Treaty of Westphalia in 1648 and from this date entirely new methods of working amber are introduced.

Danzig introduced the wooden core (only used at Königsberg earlier for games-boards) as a means by which large monumental religious items could be constructed. The term is known as *incrustation**, and again it will cause confusion to the

---

*The gemmologist usually understands incrustation to mean the securing of a stone flush with its setting, held there by pushing some of the setting over the girdle. With amber objects the amber is held from behind, not the side.

Figure 4.7 (a) Nymph and putti. *Bayerisches National museum, Munich,* (b) crouching lion, *Victoria and Albert Museum, London.*

gemmologist who would use it in a stricter context. Incrustation here means the fitting together of flat slabs of amber, over a solid, to form a large strengthened structure. On seventeenth-century examples these slabs show a strong geometric design, but in the eighteenth century they were used as random mosaic panels. The slabs were cemented to the wood with an organic glue. In many cases this glue has since dried out and the panels have become separated or lost. This has meant that much amber from this period is stored awaiting eventual restoration.

Danzig produced large quantities of religious objects: court altarpieces, crucifixes, candlesticks and small house altars. Whereas ivory or white amber had been used under clear amber previously, with the introduction of incrustation comes the introduction of pierced ivory or white amber reliefs left exposed without any form of covering. The author has found no amber object with exposed plaques prior to the mid-seventeenth century, and this is a trait of Danzig rather than of Königsberg.

There is a fine altarpiece in Florence made for the Polish Court in Danzig and dated 1669. While,not the most exciting example, it is rare to have any amber work dated and this altarpiece also shows two other features often associated with Danzig workmanship: barley-sugar twist columns and thin carved 'wings' mounted at the sides of the central section. The manner by which this piece has been dated is interesting. It carried a document in one of the inside drawers bearing the message: 'Dass Ich Unterschriebener von Heern Petro Gatoria, gutt Vollkommen undt Universehret empfangen habe, tuhe ich mit Eigener Unterschrift bezeigen. Datum Danzig den 24 Sept. Anno 1669 – Woycieck Zelesky MP; Hanns Steiniger MPia'.

In Königsberg the most important amber worker of the mid-seventeenth century was Jacob Heise. Little is known about him except that he signed and dated a very ornate nautilus cup now in the Grünes Gewölbe, Dresden. This cup is dated 1659, and another, simpler and perhaps more pleasing example exists in the Metropolitan Museum of Art, New York, dated at 1660. A third cup, again very ornate, is illustrated in Pelka (1920: Figure 81) from the Kunstgewerbe Museum, Berlin. The Dresden and the Berlin cups show highly carved white amber as a major element in the composition, and owing to this it is thought that the major work of the standing figures of the Great Elector and his wife Luise Henriette may also be by Heise, dated at between 1646 and 1667. A very elaborate bowl in the Kunsthistorisches Museum, Vienna, is also thought to be the work of Heise.

Many of the items associated with Heise have a nautical theme on some part of the object, and this interest in the sea, sea monsters and sea shells, is mirrored in other works of the same period. There is an amber salt cellar decorated with sea shells and Neptune in the Staatliche Kunstsammlungen, Kassel, while the Louvre, Paris, houses the magnificent Dolphin Bowl of Louis XIV (reigned 1643–1715.) This bowl measures 45 cm in length and is of a dull orange, opaque amber. It contains two intertwined dolphins and is supported by the figure of Triton in combat, sitting astride a dragon. The amber fountain in Florence has motifs of sea shells, dolphins and putti; although there are also areas of the design where low relief carving reminiscent of Georg Schreiber has been employed, the nautical emphasis seems to place it nearer the end of the seventeenth century rather than 1610 as usually given. It first appears on an inventory for the collection in 1670.

It must not be thought that amber was only used for major works in large quantity. In Paris (Louvre) and London (British Museum) there are two tiny examples of amber lozenges used as pocket-watch cases. The London example has a movement signed Issac Plaecier, Londoni (active 1641–1645).

Christoph Maucher settled in Danzig from Germany in 1670, and although the local guild would not admit him, his skill in figure carving so delighted the court at Brandenburg that, although he worked in Danzig, he was virtually the court-amber carver for Brandenburg. This method of work was the forerunner for others: Jacob Dobbermann at Kassel, Wilhelm Kruger at Dresden and Lorenz Spengler at Copenhagen.

Much research has been carried out on Christoph Maucher by Trusted (1984) and the pieces that could seem to be attributable to him all show superb workmanship and quality. The women are sensuous and rounded, with down-turned eyes and plump cheeks, and although the pieces are intricate in composition they do not appear cluttered. Examples of his work are to be found in the Victoria and Albert Museum, London where there are two figure groups of the Judgement of Paris (*Figure 4.8*); two more in the Staatliche Museum Preussischer Kulturbesitz, Berlin: one of the judgement of Paris and one of Perseuis and Phineus; and a similar carving of the Three Graces the Grünes Gewölbe Dresden. Trusted has identified two further sets of single figures: Judith and Jael in the Galleria e Museo Estense, Modena, and Dido and Cleopatra in the Kunsthistorisches Museum, Vienna. The only signed work by Maucher is an ivory monument dated 1700 for Leopold I of Austria and the Holy Roman Empire. The amber works cited are usually dated at between 1670 and 1700.

Figure 4.8 The judgement of Paris by Christoph Maucher. *Victoria and Albert Museum, London.*

One of the socles (bases) of the Victoria and Albert Museum figure groups has chinoiserie scenes depicted under clear amber panels. This Oriental theme probably came from a set of engravings, as similar scenes are found on a cabinet at Brunswick and on a casket at Uppsala, as well as on some of the missing panels from the amber throne. The throne of amber was commissioned by the Great Elector from Nicholas Turow at Danzig, for Leopold I of Austria. Today, only the drawings and some small fragments remain in Vienna, but it is thought that pieces may still come to light in other collections (Baer, 1982).

Devotional objects

Danzig continued with its production of devotional objects (presumably undertaken by the guild) and many house altars survive. However, the picture is not too clear for it is evident that throughout the Renaissance all centres made devotional objects, although Danzig would appear to have led production. A curious rectangular house altar is illustrated in Reineking von Bock (1981: Figure 168). This is dated 1678 and also bears the inscription: 'Friedrich Schmidt, Bernstein-Arbeiter Crottingen'. Crottingen is near Memel. This house altar is very similar to one in the Boston Fine Arts Museum and the author believes that they come from the same source.

There also occurs in the late seventeenth century a curious collection of devotional plaques where amber reliefs have been glued on to wooden or stone backings. These are thought to originate from Italy but there is no written evidence to support this claim. They may possibly have been assembled in Sicily as well as the mainland, and they may have been sections from other, larger, damaged works, sold to meet the constant Catholic demand for iconography. Examples now exist in Boston (Museum of Fine Arts), London (Victoria and Albert Museum) and Edinburgh (Royal Scottish Museum); Kassel Landesmuseum is also said to have such a plaque.

Caskets

Amber caskets and boxes were made from the time of Georg Schreiber to the mid-eighteenth century but their design fell into several periods so some distinction can be made.

The early seventeenth-century tiered casket had its ivory work protected by clear amber panels, and the remaining clear amber was worked in low relief. Any cloudy amber was left unworked and usually applied as banding. Caskets with exposed white amber or ivory pierced reliefs, and geometrically cut amber segments date from the end of the seventeenth century, and at this stage additional decoration is often added by means of amber balls, pillars, etc. at the top corners of the tiers. The late seventeenth century also brings in the single tiered box, usually on dumpy round feet, and many of these appear to be of inferior quality. What they do exhibit is true *eglomisé*, for some of the clear amber panels are incised on the back with scenes of harbour life (as usual from recognized engravings). Larger, quality caskets were still manufactured and these, in addition to finely worked ivory reliefs, often had cabochon cut, clear amber rondels of flowers and fruit in high relief. The little boxes and occasional quality secular containers continue into the early eighteenth century.

Late seventeenth to early eighteenth centuries

The late 1680s saw Frederick III of Brandenburg (to become Frederick I of Prussia in 1701) and Peter the Great of Russia rise to the thrones of Europe. Their circumstances cannot have been more different: whereas Frederick inherited an ordered, inventive nation, Peter was one of three children all favoured by different factions as

Czar, and it was some time before his mentally retarded half-brother, Ivan, and his sister, Sophia, made way for him.

However, on accession Frederick sent gifts to Russia, the bill for which still survives. The amber pieces were all made by a man from Danzig (not a guild member), Michael Redlin. Redlin received 1150 florins for a casket, 600 florins for a candelabra and 500 florins for a chessboard. Although these pieces cannot be located today, Redlin also left drawings which are illustrated in Pelka (1917). The drawing of the casket shows vases of flowers among the decoration, a pointer to late seventeenth or early eighteenth century work.

Acanthus leaves in decoration are also a feature of this period. Examples are a cup in Vienna, a tobacco container (with a porcelain miniature as a central panel) in Leningrad, cane handles in Hamburg and London, and a large mirror frame in Braunswick. This latter, measuring 63.5 cm × 43.5 cm, has always attracted a good deal of attention because on the back it carries the inscription:

'This amber mirror frame, was made by the merchant Köster from Königsberg (Prussia) during the last years of his life. He worked at it for about five years. When finished a man offered him 200 Thaler, even 100 Dukaten which he refused, thus kept the mirror until his end.'

The mirror was made in about 1700.

The Court at Kassel fostered figurework in amber, and the famous names associated with this court are Johann Christoph (d.1742), Johann Kaspar Labhard (d.1726) and Jacob Dobbermann (d.1745).

Christoph and Labhard made a series of ambers which depicted lovers or beauties lying in sea shells. These are to be found in many collections and the production must have been extensive. Sometimes, as in the examples in Copenhagen, Hamburg and Paris, the shell is raised on a stem, but more often, as in the examples now in the Kassel Landesmuseum, the objects rest without stands of any form. Two of Dobbermann's figures remain at the Kassel Landesmuseum. One depicts Cleopatra, the other an aged winged figure carrying away a young girl. The latter is signed 'JD Fz'; they are considered to have been made between 1720 and 1730.

The Danish Royal Collection of amber

Whereas the collection of amber objects at the Museo degli Argenti, Florence, is perhaps the most complete with regard to early ambers of the Renaissance, the Danish Royal Collection at the Rosenborg Castle is the richest in eighteenth-century ambers.

This collection has a few pieces of earlier date, most notably the set of plates dated 1585 which were possibly a present to King Frederick II of Denmark, and a small chandelier also from Königsberg dated at 1650. However, the collection excels in work of late seventeenth and early eighteenth century. There are amber sewing implements, toothpicks, patch boxes and burning glasses. The latter were said to have been invented in 1691 in Königsberg by Christian Porchin, who also produced spectacles by clarifying amber and removing its impurities.

As one would expect in a collection formed during this period, there is an example of a lovers' cup by Christoph or Labhard, and a casket complete with acanthus leaf decoration.

In the mid-eighteenth century, Lorenz Spengler was appointed court amber worker, and the 1740s and 1750s produced a large number of highly ornamented flacons, which run in design from baroque to rococo. Spengler himself made a large chandelier (vases of flowers are incorporated in the design) and a chess set, and was equally at home working ivory as amber.

Three of the more unusual items in the collection are minutely detailed model ships made of amber. One was made in Copenhagen in 1723, while the other two were made in Aalborg in 1760 (*Figures 4.9, 4.10 and 4.11*).

Like many other objects cited in this chapter, the collection of the Rosenborg Castle is not on view to the public, except on rare occasions, due to its fragility and the rapid deterioration caused to ambers by bright exhibition lighting.

Figure 4.9 Amber model of a ship made in Copenhagen, 1723. *Rosenborg Castle, Denmark.*

The cabinet cupboard

The cabinet cupboard was very much a product of the early eighteenth century. These cupboards, the outer doors of which open to reveal drawers in the interior, were veneered with amber on a wooden base which gave them greater strength. On some the amber 'incrustation' is kept plain with interest evolving from the varieties of amber used, while on others the surface is made up of plain pieces, reliefs high and low, pierced work and figures. One such cabinet (*Figure 4.12*), sold in London in 1961, 1973 and 1977, was described as 'the demented work of some confectioner' but it realized a very considerable sum at auction. These cabinets appear to have been special commissions, usually to mark a marriage within the royal households of northern Europe or to strengthen some tie of loyalty.

Figure 4.10 Amber model of a ship made in Aalborg, 1760. *Rosenborg Castle, Denmark.*

Figure 4.11 Amber model of a ship made in Aalborg, 1760. *Rosenborg Castle, Denmark.*

The amber room

The use of amber declined in the mid-eighteenth century as fashions altered and royal patronage was withdrawn. However, almost the last item created in this resin was perhaps the most spectacular, for during this century an entire room of amber was constructed, and acclaimed as 'the eighth wonder of the world'.

In a letter dated 2 April 1701, Frederick IV of Denmark recommended the Danish amber worker Gottfried Wolffram to Frederick I of Prussia, to design an amber room for Charlottenburg Castle near Berlin.

Wolffram worked for six years on this project but then had a serious disagreement

Figure 4.12 Cabinet cupboard, early eighteenth century.

with the German architect. In his place, Gottfried Turow and Ernst Schacht, both from Danzig, were ordered to continue work on the room and this was not completed until 1711.

By 1713 the room appears to have been assembled in Berlin, though not at Charlottenburg Castle, and in this year the newly crowned King of Prussia, Frederick William I, received a visit from the all-powerful ruler of Russia, Peter the Great. There are varying accounts as to how Peter acquired the amber room but it travelled to the new Russian capital city of St. Petersburg, being set up first in the Winter Palace and then in the New Palace.

According to records kept in Moscow, the room at this stage consisted of: two large wall panels, each inset with a framed mirror, 16 other panels, a group of shields, rosettes, pediments and corners.

When Elizabeth Petrovna became Empress of Russia in the mid-eighteenth century, she moved the amber room to the Summer Palace, 15 miles to the south at Tsarskoe Selo (*Figure 4.13*). However, the room where the amber was to be exhibited – one of a series, including a lapis lazuli room – measured 1224 square metres, whereas there was only enough amber for 55 square metres.

Accordingly, tall pier glasses on white and gold pier tables were introduced between the panels, and one wall (the window wall) was left plain to emphasize the elaborate golden amber mosaic work of the other three walls. Both 1701 and 1760 were marked on panels of amber within the room, attesting to its long and varied creation. Indeed, the work must have been longer than this for, according to the records of the Königsberg Amber Guild, five guild members were still working on it in 1763.

The room was ornamented with various amber objects (now housed in Moscow) and must have created a wondrous spectacle; especially so as in the early twentieth century Tsarskoe Selo was the first place to see electric lighting in Russia.

Figure 4.13 The world's largest amber creation – the amber room at
Tsarskoe Selo, Russia. The walls were covered with amber mosaic.

In 1941, the siege of Leningrad by German forces appeared imminent and the
Russians set about evacuating their treasures to a safer location. However, the amber
room, being difficult to handle, had been left until the Director of the Hermitage
Museum could supervise its transportation. Two huge trainloads got away by
midsummer, but the Germans took Pushkin before the room could be moved.

A special German battalion dismantled the amber room and it was transported to
the Prussian Fine Arts Museum at Königsberg under escort of a field marshal, two
captains, one NCO and six privates. Its arrival in Königsberg was the high spot in the
career of Dr Alfred Rhode, author of what even today is considered the definitive
book on ambers of this period.

The excitement of Rhode can be imagined as he reassembled the room on the third
floor of Königsberg Castle. The Germans had always felt very patriotic about amber,
and considered the room as now back where it belonged on German soil. Only a year
later the British started to bomb Königsberg, and twice hit the outer rim of the castle.
The room was hastily dismantled and Rhode wrote to owners of castles to the west,
and there is evidence that he made visits looking for possible safer hiding places.

The panels were then repacked, this time for 'long transportation', and piled in the
castle yard, apparently bound for Saxony but they never arrived.

The panels had been repacked in January 1945 and the Russians took Königsberg
in April. Neither the Germans nor the Russians appear to know what happened to the
room, but of course there is much suspicion on both sides. Friesen, provincial
custodian, vanished immediately, and Rhode and his wife died together in suspicious
circumstances late in 1945. With these people probably died the evidence as to the
whereabouts of the amber room for, despite thousands of pounds spent on subse-
quent research, the trail to find the eighth wonder of the world is cold.

Rumours were rife in London in 1985 that amber stockpiled to rebuild the amber
room had been stolen and smuggled into western Europe. Apparent Polish sources

offered such amber for sale in Copenhagen on several occasions. If this is really the case, it is unfortunate as the amber for the reproduction of the room is probably all natural, but the pressures of commerce may necessitate that for today's buyers this will be clarified and sold off in very small amounts, with larger pieces being cut up or even recycled as pressed pieces, so as not to arouse suspicion.

Bibliography

ASCHENGREEN PIACENTI, K., 'Due Altari in Ambra al Museo degli Argenti,' *Bollettino d'Arte*, December, 163–166 (1966)

BAER, W., 'Ein Bernsteinstuhl für Kaiser Leopold I. Ein Geschenk des Kurfürsten Friedrich Wilhelm von Brandenburg', *Jahrbuch der Kunsthistorischen Sammlungen in Wien* (1982)

DAVIS, F., 'Talking about sale rooms', *Country Life*, 21 March (1974)

GAY, V., *Glossaire Archéologique du Moyen Age et de la Renaissance*, Vol. I, p. 28, Paris (1887)

GRABOWSKA, J., *Polnischer Bernstein*, Warsaw; also available in English (1982). Gives long-needed emphasis to works of art which originate in Danzig rather than in Königsberg.

PELKA, O., *Die Meister der Bernsteinkunst*, Nuremberg (1917). Detailed research on this narrow topic. A unique opportunity to have readily available, what today would probably be an academic dissertation rather than a publication

PELKÁ, O., *Bernstein*, Richard Carl Schmidt & Co., Berlin (1920). A forerunner to Rhode; useful illustrations of objects since lost in the Second World War

REINEKING VON BOCK, G., *Bernstein. Das Gold der Ostsee*, Verlag Callweg, Munich (1981). Richly illustrated; good source for comparing designs and styles

RHODE, A., *Bernstein, ein Deutscher Werkstoff. Seine Künstlerische Verarbeitung vom Mittelatler bis zum 18. Jahrhundert*, Berlin (1937). The authoritative book on this period. A chilling memorial

TRUSTED, M., 'Four Amber Statuettes by Christoph Maucher', *Pantheon*, **XLII**, 245–250 (1984)

TRUSTED, M., *Catalogue of the European Ambers in the Victoria and Albert Museum*, London (1985). Contains much fresh research

WILLIAMSON, G. C., *The Book of Amber*, pp. 43–44, quoting Maccall unpublished papers, Ernest Benn, London (1932)

PLATE 1

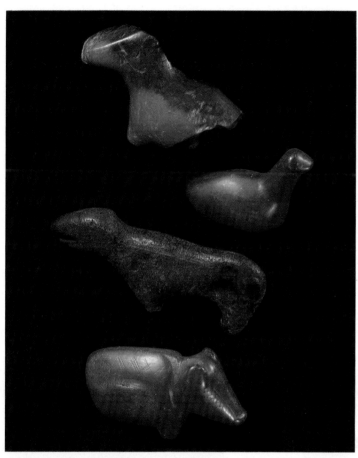

a Mesolithic Hunting Amulets. 7000 BC. The
oldest three-dimensional works of art in Northern
Europe. Courtesy Jørgen Jensen,
Nationalmuseet, Copenhagen

b South Italic Amber Carving. Possibly depicting
the Goddess Athena. Late 6th or early 5th century
BC. Courtesy the Trustees of the British Museum,
London

c Central European Iron Age Grave Group.
Courtesy of Erzebet Jerem, Archeological
Institute of the Hungarian Academy of Sciences,
Budapest

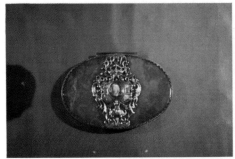

b

c

PLATE 2

a Small personal items made of amber. Late 17th or early 18th century. Courtesy Royal Danish Collection, Rosenborg Castle

b Candlesticks, North German 17th century. Courtesy Sotheby's London

c Dressing Cabinet. North German 17th century. Courtesy Sotheby's London

d Detail of a North German altar piece, 17th century. Courtesy Museo degli Argenti, Palazzo Pitti, Florence

a

PLATE 3

b

a Amber and silver brooch. 1985. Courtesy Waldemar Goralski, Essen

b Amber and silver pendant. 1985. Courtesy Waldemar Goralski, Essen

c Range of amber necklaces

d Samples of Baltic amber purchased in Denmark in 1985. Note Baltic amber can occur in red tones, although they are rare. Private Collection

e Natural cloudy Baltic amber, sales display in a tourist resort, 1985, Jutland. This is an important record, as the majority of outlets selling amber today retail amber that has been clarified or altered in form

f Jewellery made from cast phenolic resin, often mistaken for natural fossil resin. Private Collection

c

d

e

f

a

b

c

d

PLATE 4

a A pair of Lion Dogs or Temple Guardians. The simpler example was probably carved locally in Burma, and the more recent, complex ornament in China. Both are executed in Burmite, and show typical colouring. Private Collection

b Chinese flat plaques used as dress ornaments. 19th century. Private Collection

c Pendant with two dragons, Iron Crutch Li, and a peacock. Three 19th century examples of Burmite, carved in China. Private Collection

d Meershaum Pipe with amber mouthpiece. Made in Vienna, 19th century. Private Collection

e Two 19th century amber brooches. Most examples have brass or base metal fitments. Private collection

e

PLATE 5

a Arnold Buffum's famous casket, set with Simetite cabochons. Late 19th century. Boston Museum of Fine Arts, USA

b Colour range of Simetite. Courtesy Fratelli Fecarotta, Catania, Sicily

c 19th century illustration to Buffum's book *The Tears of the Heliades*, depicting one of the necklaces left to the Boston Museum of Fine Arts in 1901, which form part of an extensive collection of Simetite

d Modern brooch made in Italy, set with a Simetite cabochon. Courtesy Fratelli Fecarotta, Catania, Sicily

e Edwardian brooch and earrings, apparently of red Simetite. Many examples of this type are in fact coloured Succinite, but they have retained their value as historical examples of a period of fashion

a

PLATE 6

b

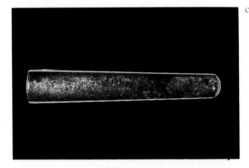

c

a Romanian necklace, photographed in the house of Dom Christian, Colti, Romania

b Romanian necklace; note the typical colouring and design. Courtesy London Gem Testing Laboratory

c Cigarette holder of the rare 'mother of pearl' varient of Romanian amber or Roumanite. Courtesy British Museum of Natural History, London

d View from a mine in Colti, near Buzau, Romania

e The mine viewed at Colti penetrates the hillside in two galleries to a depth necessitating the provision of air pumps

e

d

PLATE 7

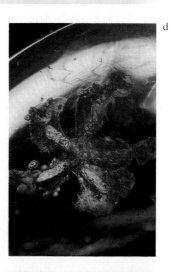

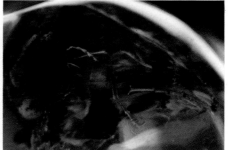

a Two animal figures from the Dominican Republic. Private Collection

b Typical jewellery sold in the Dominican Republic; note the fitments. Private Collection

c View of the terrain near La Cumbre, Dominican Republic. The shallow mines are cut into the exposed sandstone cliff

d Flora inclusion, Dominican Amber. Courtesy Ken Scarratt. Private Collection

e Insect in Dominican Amber; note the raised layer of amber caused by the Inclusion. Courtesy Ken Scarratt. Private Collection

f Insect in Dominican Amber. Courtesy Ken Scarratt. Private Collection

PLATE 8

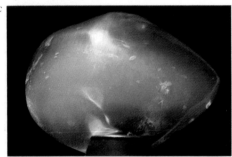

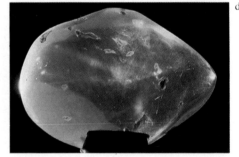

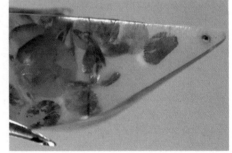

a Jewellery using Copal or recent resin in place of fossil resin. The surface is covered in white crumbling powder. Private Collection

b Bees in Kauri Gum. Courtesy Neil Hanna, Gemmological Association of New Zealand

c Dominican Amber showing natural fluorescence. Private Collection

d The same piece of Dominican Amber under different lighting conditions (refracted light rather than reflected light)

e Sun-spangle inclusions, induced by quick cooling of clarified amber. Courtesy London Gem Testing Laboratory

f 'Surface colour treated amber' a recent product from Idar Oberstein. Courtesy London Gem Testing Laboratory

Chapter 5

Medicinal usage of amber

Amber has been heralded as the panacea for all ills. This faith in the curative or amuletic power of fossil resin appears with earliest man. Lumps of amber bearing shallow depressions from Palaeolithic sites are thought to have been treasured as the dwelling places of spirits (Hoerrie's opinion cited by Kunz, 1971).

Throughout history, man has used amber for curing in its widest sense: as a treasured lump, as grains of powder to be consumed, rubbed on the body as embrocation, or burned as purifying incense. One of the seldom quoted meanings of the ancient Greek word for amber, *electrum*, is 'I protect' (Frondel, 1968).

The pre-Christian Italic peoples bored curious holes in their amber amulets, often subsequently plugging the holes with amber of a different hue. Perhaps the amber originally withdrawn was used for medicinal purposes; certainly the holes do not appear to have been bored at random and occur most frequently on head pendants or on larger religious pieces (*Figure 5.1*).

Figure 5.1 Female head pendant carved from a rough lump of amber. Holes bored into the surface were filled with a darker coloured amber. *British Museum, London.*

Amber was definitely linked with a connotation of fertility and protection from the evil eye. Apart from the amber heads mentioned above, the other predominant designs were the bullae (bottle or pear) shape, cowrie shell and ram's head.

The first lengthy treatise to have survived, where amber is given considerable mention, is from Volume 37 of Pliny's *Natural History of Precious Stones*. The following was written in the first century AD (translation as given in Williamson, 1932):

'Amber is not without its utility in a medicinal point of view; though it is not for this reason that the women are so pleased with it. It is beneficial for infants, attached to the body in the form of an amulet; and according to [the Greek writer] Callistratus, it is good for any age, as a preventive of delirium and as a cure for strangury, either taken in drink or attached as an amulet to the body. This last author, too, has invented a new variety of amber, giving it the name of "Chryselectrum" to an amber of golden colour, and which presents the most beautiful tints in the morning . . . This last kind, worn upon the neck is a cure for fevers and other diseases, and triturated with honey and oil of roses, it is good for maladies of the ears. Beaten up with Attic honey, it is good for dimness of sight, and the powder of it, either taken by itself or with gum mastic in water, is remedial for diseases of the stomach.

At the present day we see the female peasantry in the countries that lie beyond the river (Po) wearing amber, principally as an ornament no doubt, but on account of its remedial virtues as well, for amber it is generally believed is good for the affections of the tonsillary glands and fauces, the various kinds of water in the vicinity of the Alps being apt to produce disease in the human throat.' (A high rate of goitre and the more serious cretinism has been recorded until recent times from this area.)

There is a gap in the writings about amber in the early Medieval period but from the sixteenth century onwards there are frequent references to the efficacy of this apparently unique fossil resin.

The self-proclaimed Duke Albert of Prussia was elected Grand Master of the Teutonic Knights in 1511. This body held the monopoly on Baltic amber sales, and the Duke was keen to secure the maximum revenue that was possible. Two forms of amber were hard to dispose of: the smaller pieces and white amber. This latter, full of holes, is softer to work and does not take a high polish. Two court physicians were accordingly set the task of producing scientific papers to back amber as a universal remedy for everything from impotence to hysteria. There is no surprise, knowing this background, that Drs Aurifaber and Göbel found powdered amber to be of great benefit – and particularly recommended the white variety.

Forty years later, these writings had commanded such respect that Duke Albert, when transferring the Amber Monopoly to a family of Danzig merchants (the Jaskis), retained the rights to all white amber found along the coast.

Camillus Leonardus wrote in *Speculum Lapidum:*

'Amber naturally restrains the flux of the belly, is an efficacious remedy for all disorders of the throat. It is good against poison. If laid on the breast of a wife when she is asleep, it makes her confess all her evil deeds. It fastens teeth that are loosened, and by smoke of it poisonous insects are driven away.' (Budge, 1961)

The use of amber was widespread all over Europe. In Germany, Martin Luther carried a lump of amber in his pocket to ward off kidney stones (d'Aulaire, 1974). In Scotland, Leslie wrote that the women 'used amber hung round their necks to

decorate themselves and also hung it on their infants to protect them from evil'
(Leslie: *De Orogine, Moribus et Rebus getis Scotorum*, 1578). In England, the
physician Bulleyn (cousin of Queen Anne Boleyn) prescribed:

'two drachmes of white perles, two little peeces of saphyre; jacinthe, corneline, emeraulds,
granettes, of each an ounce; readed coral, amber, shaving of ivory of each two drachmes,
thin peeces of gold and silver, of each half a scruple.' (Schweighimer, 1968)

Sac Frères in London once handled a ring reputed to have belonged to Lucrezia
Borgia. The shank was plain gold and six claws held in place an intricately carved
amber snake, its head raised with forked tongue ready to strike. The amber was of a
brilliant red, with a diameter of 2.5 cm. On the underside was a round knob which
released poison from a hidden chamber within the setting (Hunga, 1977). The lady
was obviously not taking any chances for amber was also said to have the power of
detecting poison: 'for then an appearance like the rainbow flies to and fro in the
vessel, attended by the cracking of flame'.

'Amber is esteemed the best for physic use, and is thought to be of great power and for
against many diseases, and against vertigo and asthmatic paroxysmes, against catarrhes,
against diseases of the stomach and to free it from sufferings and putrefactions, and against
diseases of the heart, against plagues, venoms and contagions. It is used either in distempers
of men and women, married or unmarried, or in the distempers of children.' (Thomas
Nicols, 1659)

'Amber heats and dries, therefore prevails against most diseases of the head; it helps violent
coughs, helps consumption of the lungs, spitting of blood, the whites in women. It stops
bleeding at the nose, helps difficulty of urine; you may take ten or twenty grains at a time.'
(Culpepper's *Dispensatory*, 1654)

'The falling sickness, take half a drachm of choice amber, powder it very fine, and take it
once a day in a quantity of a pint of white wine, for seven or eight days, successively ... If
further treatment is needed take bits of amber, and in a colsestool put them upon a chafing
dish of live charcoal, over which let the patient sit, and receive the fumes. (See also
Ambergris).' (Salmon, 1679)

Meanwhile back in the Baltic new ideas were being promulgated to boost the desire
for amber. At the turn of the seventeenth century, Christian Porschin of the
Königsberg Guild, by 'using a special process of gentle heating in linseed oil to render
the amber clear and transparent', started to manufacture burning glasses and even
ground spectacle lenses.

Although amber may have been turned into the exotic by the few, it remained the
universal cure-all of the masses. (*Figure 5.2*).

'Many are the excellent virtues of amber, especially when taken inwardly in a cold state of
the brain, in catarrhs, in the head-ach, sleepy and convulsive disorders, in the suppression of
menses, hysterical and hypochondriacal affections, and in hemorrhages or bleedings.'

In Scotland, an amber bead 2.2 cm in diameter and 1.3 cm thick, from Galloway,
belonged to Carnochan, a celebrated eighteenth-century smuggler. He was said to
have taken it from some Adders who hotly pursued him on his horse across
Auchencairn Bay. Carnoch wore the amber on a ribbon around his neck as a
talisman, and used it for curing various diseases, and for averting 'the evil eye'. It had

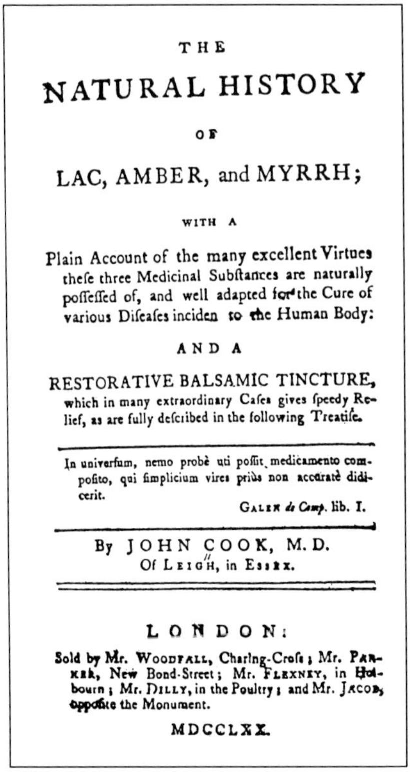

THE

NATURAL HISTORY

OF

LAC, AMBER, and MYRRH;

WITH A

Plain Account of the many excellent Virtues
thefe three Medicinal Subftances are naturally
poffeffed of, and well adapted for the Cure of
various Difeafes inciden to the Human Body:

AND A

RESTORATIVE BALSAMIC TINCTURE,
which in many extraordinary Cafes gives fpeedy Relief, as are fully defcribed in the following Treatife.

In univerfum, nemo probè uti poffit medicamento com-
pofito, qui fimplicium vires priùs non accuratè didi-
cerit.
                          GALEN de Comp. lib. I.

By J O H N C O O K, M. D.
Of L E I G H, in E s s e x.

L O N D O N:

Sold by Mr. WOODFALL, Charing-Crofs; Mr. PAR-
KER, New Bond-Street; Mr. FLEXNEY, in Hol-
bourn; Mr. DILLY, in the Poultry; and Mr. JACOB,
oppofite the Monument.

MDCCLXX.

Figure 5.2 Front page of *The Natural History of Lac, Amber and Myrrh.*

to be dipped three times in water, which was then given to the sick child or animal to drink. The bead was lost one day while the smuggler was in his garden but apparently, when found many years later by his grandchildren, its strange powers had departed (Black, 1893).

Also in Scotland, on the Isle of Lewis, a small round semi-transparent stone, having the appearance of amber, was described in 1874 as possessing extraordinary powers,

'both in regard to man and beast when they happen to be serpent bitten ... It has been sent to all the villages for many miles round about, and was in special request when the ordinary serpent-stones failed in effecting a cure.' (Black, 1893)

The use of amber as a cure for both man and beast appears to be widespread. Frondel (1968) records that amber was used as a fumigant with gunpowder in stalls which had housed ailing horses.

In country areas, the belief that amber could cure problems concerning the eyes remained dominant throughout the nineteenth century. In north-east Scotland 'an amber bead, vernacularly called "lammer"* was commonly used to remove a chaff from the eye of man or beast, and a necklace of the same material was worn as a cure for diseases of the eyes' (Gregor, 1881). Henderson (1879) reported: 'I have myself

*See poem at end of chapter.

seen and handled a talisman from the Tweedside. It was called a lammer-bead and wondrous were the cures it wrought, in the witch-woman's hands; when drawn over the inflamed eyes or sprained limbs.' These beads were often strung with red thread and thought to repel witches:

'Black luggie, lammer bead,
Rowan tree, and red thread,
put the witches to their speed.' (Chambers, 1847)

A variant occurs in the folklore of Ireland:

'In Ireland pearls upon the eye are said to be removed by an amber bead, the tenth upon a rosary rubbed on the eye. The wise woman of the village will show the amber bead, with a white substance adhering, which she affirms is the pearl removed by the mystic attraction of the amber.' (Wilde, 1890)

The nineteenth century was a period of great and rapid change and nowhere does this show so evidently as in the great divide between science and folklore. The components of amber had at last been separated on a regular basis and in the 1898 edition of the *United States Dispensatory*, rectified oil of amber is listed for use internally as an antispasmodic, and externally as a counter-irritant in attacks of rheumatism (Frondel, 1968).

In China, syrup of amber was frequently used as a sedative – it was made of succinic acid and opium and one imagines was very effective. Eau de Luce – oil of amber and ammonia – was used extensively in fainting fits, and the medical fraternity took its powers very seriously:

'Du Succin employé dans la coqueluche, les convulsions et les coliques des enfants pendant la première dentition.' (Danet, 1862)

'Observations et expériences sur la vertu de l'ambre jaune dans une maladie nerveuse de form convulsive.' (Gerard, 1842)

We may scoff today that in Russia the nurse would wear an amber necklace so that sickness would not fall on nurse or child, or that an amber bead was often concealed in the folds of an infant's inner garments: 'the bead ever-famous for its mystic virtues in repelling the invisible operations of fairy influence supposed to have been exercised upon these defenceless beings'. It is a sobering thought that the shahs of Iran traditionally wore an amber bead to protect them from assassination, but none was found when the Crown Jewels of Iran passed to the State following the deposition of the last Shah.

The late nineteenth century also covered the great expansion of amber used as a germicidal agent in smoking requisites (*Figure 5.3*). The idea of using amber in the hookah, Turkish nahpiril and European pipe, stems from a belief that amber stopped the passing of disease. No doubt browsers of Cope's Smoke Room Booklet: *Amber, All About It*, were also relieved to read the advertisement: 'Cope's cigarettes are made by English girls, not made in continental prisons, not made in the slums of Cairo or Constantinople' (Haddow, 1891).

Just before the First World War we learn that: 'The Managing Director of Harrods stores in London, Mr Richard Burbidge had been good enough to inform me that his

Figure 5.3 Turkish chibouk/European parasol handle.

firm sell amber at the present time, set as a jewel, to prevent cold and for the cure of rheumatism' (Lebour, 1914–15). Between the wars, Dr Williamson tells us: 'distilled amber, yielding a pungent, acrid, but not unpleasant oil, known as Oil of Amber or Oil of Succinite, is still recognised as a potent ingredient in various embrocations'. Also:

> 'A well-known chemist has declared, in my own hearing, that his wife had suffered from asthma all her life until five years ago, when she expressed a desire to wear a string of amber, and since wearing this she has not experienced the slightest symptom of her former trouble.' (Williamson, 1932)

The same year as *The Book of Amber* appeared in London, there is a note in the USA of 'a volatile oil extracted from amber used medicinally in cases of infantile convulsions' (Bureau of Mines, 1934) and in Germany it is understood that amber vessels (made of ambroid rather than natural resin) were being used during blood transfusions, the amber having less effect on changing the temperature of the blood than glass or stone.

I have, in my own collection, a fine plastic (cast phenolic) necklace, purchased from an elderly lady at Clapham Common. She assured me that the beads on this particular necklace were uneven in shape because her late husband used to rub them so vigorously during asthma attacks. As the family were apparently unaware that the necklace was not amber, the placebo effect obviously works very well.

Today, amber has a widespread, if occasional, usage in many branches of medicine, especially that of homeopathy. Perhaps the most important use claimed for amber is as a constituent of lammer wine – a concoction of unspecified ingredients in which amber was dissolved. This was said to be the elixir of immortality (*Hislop Anecdotes*, 1874, ix):

> 'Drink ae coup o' the lammer-wine,
> An the tear is nae mair in your e'e.
>
> An drink twae coups o' the lammer-wine,
> Nae dule nor pine ye'll dree.
>
> An drink three coups o' the lammer-wine,
> Your mortal life's awa.
>
> An drink four coups o' the lammer-wine,
> Ye'll turn a fairy sma'.
>
> An drink five coups o' the lammer-wine,
> O joys ye've rowth an' wale.

An drink six coups o' the lammer-wine,
Ye'll ring ower hill and dale.

An drink seven coups o' the lammer-wine,
Ye may dance on the milky way.

An drink eight coups o' the lammer-wine,
Ye may ride on the fire flaught blae.

An drink nine coups o' the lammer-wine,
Your end day ye'll nier see.

An the nicht is gane, an' the day has come,
An will never set to thee.'

Bibliography

BLACK G. F., 'Scottish charms and amulets', *Proceedings of the Scottish Antiquarian Society*, Vol. III, Scottish Museum of Antiquities, Edinburgh (1893)

BUDGE, E. A., *Amulets and Talismans*, reprinted by University Books, New York (1961)

CHAMBERS, R., *Popular Rhymes of Scotland*, Vol. VII, Scottish Museum of Antiquities, Edinburgh (1847)

CULPEPPER, T., *Dispensaroris*, British Museum Library, London (1654)

D'AULAIRE, E. and D'AULAIRE O., 'For ever amber', *Readers Digest*, December (1974)

DANET, *Bulletin de l'Academie de Medeane, Paris*, Vol. XXVIII (1862); in: Denny Papers, Mineralogy Library, British Museum of Natural History, London

FRONDEL, J., 'Amber facts and fancies', *Economic Botany*, **22**, No. 4 (1968)

GERARD, A., *Journal des Connaissance Medico-Chirgicales, Paris*, **IX**, Part 2 (1842)

GREGOR, W., *Folklore of North East Scotland*, Scottish Museum of Antiquities, Edinburgh (1881)

HADDOW, J. G., *'Amber, All About It'*, Cope's Smoke Room Booklets, No. 7, Liverpool (1891)

HISLOP, *Anecdotes*, Vol. IX (1874)

HENDERSON, W., *Folklore of the Northern Counties of England and the Borders* (1879)

HUNGA, R., *The Magic of Amber*, NAG Press, London (1977)

KUNZ, G. F. *Curious Lore of Precious Stones*, reprinted by Dover Publications, New York (1971)

LEBOUR, N., Amber and jet in ancient burials, *Transactions of the Dumfriesshire and Galloway Natural History Society* (1914–1915)

NICHOLS, T., *Gemmarius Fidelius, or the Faithful Lapidary*, British Museum Library, London (1659)

SALMON, W., *Family Dictionary*, British Museum Library, London (1679)

SCHWEIGHIMER, W., 'The magical power of jewels', *Jeweller's Circular, Keystone*, **139** (1968)

US BUREAU OF MINES *Information Circular*, No. 6789 (1934)

WILDE, LADY, *Ancient Cures, Charms and Usages in Ireland* (1890)

WILLIAMSON, G. C., *The Book of Amber*, Ernest Benn, London (1932)

Chapter 6

Adulteration: amber of the nineteenth and twentieth centuries

The nineteenth century

Until the mid-nineteenth century all Baltic amber was *sea amber* or *sea stone*, that is, it was collected direct from the sea or its environs. Shallow holes had been dug among the sand dunes but no organized, systematic mining had taken place.

The methods of winning amber from the sea were perilous and unsophisticated. There is a famous early illustration (*Figure 6.1*) of two amber gatherers, dressed in heavy cuirasses (i.e. leather body armour). What is seldom explained about the

Figure 6.1 Amber gatherers of the fifteenth century.

illustration is that the fire at the top of the snow-clad hill was to melt the outer garments as they often froze solid on the fishermen.

The amber was gathered immediately after a winter storm as it lay tangled in the seaweed; this was known as *strand amber*. In the nineteenth century in England, the amber boom was probably of the reverse origin: 'it must be remembered that were it not for the constant gathering of sea weed for manure, nearly all the (amber) pieces would be overlooked and destroyed by the waves' (Read, 1884).

Today, such amber is eagerly sought, by lamplight if necessary, at the turn of the high tide but it is agreed all across the Baltic that the amount thrown up in the mid-twentieth century is little in comparison to earlier times.

In calmer weather, amber was loosened from the sea bottom with the aid of a pole, up to six metres in length, on the end of which was a metal two-pronged fork or a little net. The gatherers either waded out into the shallows or went out by boat to scoop the amber up from deeper water. This was a tiresome process, and the water had to be extremely clear for it to be profitable. This amber was called *schöpfstein*, or drawn amber. Bauer (1904) comments that the latter method was only undertaken on the north-west corner of Samland, not on the coast of West Prussia. The tools used in this process are illustrated in *Figure 6.2*.

The nineteenth century opened with the prospects for the sale of amber at a very low ebb.

In 1811, the Prussian State handed its prerogative over to an agent, initially for an

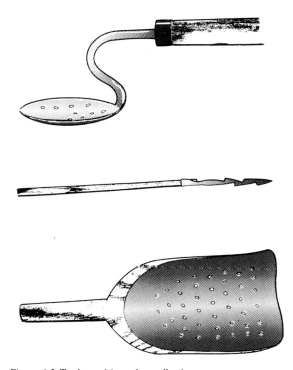

Figure 6.2 Tools used in amber collection.

annual payment of 6000 groschen. The remaining amber guilds of Königsberg and Stolp were placated by an arrangement which secured them an indemnity.

A book published at this period (Rees, 1819) states: 'when amber was more in request than it is now . . . by the change in fashion amber is little used as an ornament in Europe. Trinkets are however still valued in Turkey and the East.'

The compulsory collection of amber by the local inhabitants came to an end, but the lessees, then concentrated on digging for the resin in pits. There appears to have been a great deal of abuse and in 1923 this first lease expired.

The price of amber then fell further due to unrest in Turkey, and the lessees again faced opposition from local people as by now the beaches where the amber was to be found had also become popular with visitors. The restrictions on access and the pit diggings naturally did little for this nascent tourist industry.

In 1836, to the delight of all concerned, King Friedrich Wilhelm III set in motion laws to grant leases to the local inhabitants rather than one large lessee. Fifty-eight districts were granted such licences and the pit diggings increased at such a rate that problems arose from the increase of the population moving into the area to take advantage of the boom.

The position of amber as a profitable commodity made a complete turn-around in the last quarter of the nineteenth century due to the endeavours of one firm, that of

Figue 6.3 A display of amber necklaces auctioned at Sothebys during May 1984.

Messrs Stantien and Becker, who started at a time when amber had largely lost its popularity within Europe: 'In our times the part of the amber furnished by the Baltic finds its way to China to be used for burning in powder as incense (very little being now worked up in Europe as to ornaments)'.

In 1874:

'Yellow amber cut in facets or simply in beads for bracelets and necklaces, was in fashion some years ago. At the present day it is chiefly used in the East by the Turks, Egyptians, Arabs, Persians and the natives of India, to ornament their pipes, arms, the saddles and bridles of their horses. In Europe it is still used for the mouthpieces of pipes.'

The key to the success of Stantien and Becker lies in their perception of the market. They ascertained that the future for amber was in smoking requisites rather than as jewellery, and that if a great demand could be nurtured, it would need a consistent supply of raw materials.

In 1855, it was noticed that during work on the basin of the Kurische Haff lagoon much amber had been exposed among the silt. In 1861, Stantien and Becker offered to drain part of the lagoon at their own expense if the government would permit them the proceeds of the amber harvest. In the following years a large dredging operation developed around the town of Schwarzort. The number of employees at one stage reached 1000 men, and in 1883 the dredged amber from this area amounted to 75 546 kg.

In 1870, Stantien and Becker received the contract to dig for amber around the

Figure 6.4 Blue earth containing amber was taken to the surface at the East Prussian mines for separation, Samland 1930.

Figure 6.5 High-pressure water jets used to separate amber from the blue earth found in this East Prussian mine.

coast at Warnicken and Palmnicken. By the end of that decade they had been granted permission to sink a mine at Palmnicken and this site, which later included a varnish factory, employed 900 people.

Stantien and Becker even turned their sights to the hazardous proposition of diving for amber. They had made the highest bid to the government for diving rights in 1869, and this diving was centred on Brüsterort.

Williamson (1932) covers this period extensively and gives the following figures for the production of amber through the Stantien and Becker enterprise for the year 1883:

Through mining	88 031 kg
Through dredging	75 546 kg
Through diving	2 576 kg

It might be said that the rise of the firm of Stantien and Becker was simply a matter of luck and chance. However, this was also a period of experiment and in the late 1870s the patents that are relevant to the manufacture of adulterated ambers start to make their appearance. These were obviously in direct competition with the natural raw amber controlled by Stantien and Becker.

1879:   Schrader, E. and Dumke, O. Verhahren und Apparat zum schmelzen von Bernstein. Method and apparatus for melting amber. Pine resin was added and the amber was melted with superheated steam. Patent 4679 (Germany).

1887:   Karpeles, J. Improvement in the process and means for concreting amber shavings. Pressure moulds were used at temperatures of approximately 300°C. Patent 688 (Britain).

1886/7:   Lehmann, R., Burger, C. F. and Seifert, F. J. Neuerung an dem im Patent 9444 geschützten von Copal und Bernstein. Melting is accomplished in conical vessels surrounded in jackets carrying highly superheated steam. Patent 40 892 (Germany).

1891:   Beck, H. Improved manufacture of hard natural resins as substitutes for natural resins, such as copal, amber and the like. The resins are combined with 'equivalent proportions of mixtures of alcohols, especially glycerol, phenol and sugars' and with metallic oxides. Patent 9747 (Britain).

1892:   Egge, F. Method of manufacture of large articles from small pieces of amber. Amber is pressed at 240–250°C for 12–30 minutes in steel forms. Patent 66 863 (Germany).

1892:   Haller, P. Method for the manufacture of imitation amber. 'Objects carved in bone acquire the appearance of amber if boiled in oil with the addition of some potassium dichromate until the oil foams.' Patent 70 211 (Germany).

Then, as today, as soon as new methods of alteration were announced, extensive work had to be undertaken to find ways of differentiating one form of 'amber' from another. Thus, alongside these patents were published:

1884:   Hanausek, E., 'Das Färben des Bernsteins' (Colouring of amber). *Industrie-Blätter*, **21**, 37. Can be dyed with oil-soluble natural dyes (dragon's blood, alizarin, purpurin, indigo) by heating in an oil-bath containing the dye to 150–200°C.

1887:   Klebs, R., 'Uber Farbe und Imitation des Bernsteins' (On the colour and imitation of amber), *Schriften der Phys. Okon. Gesellsch. Königsburg*, **28**.

1889:   Weiss, G. and Erckmann, A. Sur les propriétés optiques de l'ambre natural et de l'ambre faux. (Natural amber shows double refraction under crossed Nicol prisms. Pressed amber shows this, but is marked by a lack of uniformity.)

1897:   Dahms, P. Further notes on the clarification of succinite. (Rape-seed oil and sand-bath methods.)

1898:   Dahms, P. An old method of artificially opacifying succinite. (Boiled in salt water.) Beck says this does not work.

1899:   Conwentz, H. Artificially coloured ambroid. 'Red, blue, light-green and heliotrope.'

1899:   Helm, O. Ambroid can be distinguished from natural amber by the difference under polarized light.

Ambroid

Spiller Imitations, or ambroid, first came on to the market in Vienna in 1881. By this means, small chips of amber were pressed hydraulically through a sieve in a steel mould, and the resulting cake could then be cut to form the mouthpieces for pipes and cigarette holders (*Figure 6.6*).

The pressed amber thus obtained could be produced in all the varieties in which natural amber occurs. However, the following should be observed; the bubbles in natural amber tend to be rounded, whereas in pressed amber they are elongated due to the production process. Also, in the partly clear and partly cloudy amber the differentiation between the two is in feather configurations. This is pretty but not a natural occurrence. Bauer (1904) observed in addition: 'at the junction of the turbid and clear portions there is ... in transmitted light a yellowish-red colour, which in reflected light and against a dark background changes to blue'. It is also recorded that pressed amber, when clear, can give the impression of the mixing of two liquids, with internal swirl marks. Bauer continues: 'between 600 and 700 hundredweight of pressed amber is now produced annually (1904) and the material fetches from 25s to 30s per pound [*Figure 6.7*]. It is used chiefly in the manufacture of cheap articles for

Figure 6.6 Making pressed amber in Poland, 1983.

Figure 6.7 Examples of late nineteenth century clarified pressed amber jewellery.

the use of smokers, and recently in the manufacture of beads for exportation to Africa.'

As explained elsewhere, pressed amber and natural amber can be separated by the gemmologist by using a polariscope to monitor the interference figures within the amber.

The twentieth century

According to Kunz (1971), the state bought out Stantien and Becker in 1899 due to their 'unpopularity'. This may, however, have been a somewhat biased view as Kunz was working with Professor Klebs, of the Prussian Department of Trade and Industry, on an extensive exhibition for the World's Fair of 1904.

The value of amber used during the year 1902 was given as follows:

Austria	1 193 141 DM
USA	834 522 DM
Germany	706 856 DM
France	121 713 DM
Turkey	75 214 DM
Britain	48 328 DM
Holland	1 723 DM

The consumption of amber in Austria was largely made up of smoking requisites manufactured in Vienna (*Figure 6.8*).

Figure 6.8 Smoking requisites, including part-worked forms.

1900 also sees the peak in activity for the extraction of kauri gum in New Zealand. At this time, over 20 000 gum diggers worked in what was Auckland Province's most valuable export. Over 10 000 tons were marketed in 1900, 70% of which was used in Europe and the USA for the production of varnish. The remaining 30% was used for a variety of other purposes, among which was the blending of kauri or copal (i.e. recent gums) with harder fossil resin.

1907: Spiller, F. Amber substitutes. Copal heated with water at pressures of 16–20 atmospheres. Acid, alkaline, or neutral additions may be made to the water. Patent 207 744 (Germany).

1911: Spiller, F. Converting copal into a mass resembling natural amber. After freeing copal from its crust, it is softened with carbon disulphide and heated uniformly in air-tight compressed forms. Patent 247 734 (Germany).

1913: Bahket, J. Artificial amber. Copal is dissolved in acetone with or without the addition of dyes, kneaded until the acetone is volatilized, then melted at 300°C and poured into forms where it is allowed to cool under pressure.

These leave us in some confusion. The name Spiller is usually associated with pre-forms of pressed amber, i.e. ambroid, yet these patents are for a vastly different material based on non-fossil gum. Also, by 1910 the larger pieces of kauri at least had been extracted, and the chips and dust that remained were being used for a finishing process for linoleum.

The production of natural amber, expecially in the Samland area, continued despite this increase in artificial or adulterated products. From 1910, the blue earth was cut away and transported elsewhere for the sorting process, rather than mined. By this means large quantities were available. Williamson (1932) gave a Baltic production of 220 000 tons, but throughout the twentieth century all figures for the production of amber must be taken as only approximate, as figures for pressed and clarified ambers are included with that for natural amber.

At the turn of the century, amber was used usually as plain round beads, or cabochon cut in the new, more naturalistic designs of jewellery. This often employed silver in its own right, rather than as a second-rate, cheaper substance. Amber of the period, set in gold, can be found but it is not very common. In Denmark, Georg Jensen and his followers experimented fairly extensively with the use of amber (*Figure 6.9*). Parallel with this development of art nouveau came the vogue, at least in Königsberg itself, for the production of furniture which employed amber as an inlay.

Figure 6.9 Silver, parcel-gilt and amber sugar caster (17.3 cm high), designed by Anton Rosen and executed by George Jensen, Copenhagen 1908. *Christies, Geneva.*

In the 1930s, the State Manufacturers in Königsberg produced a series of very fine commemorative pieces using flat slabs of amber. The fine design and execution of these pieces, nearly all now in German museums (for illustrations *see* Reineking von Bock, 1981), should not be confused with the 'seaside trade' type of amber slab article which is more frequently encountered.

Today

At the time of writing, amber jewellery has reached one of its all-time lows with regard to newly manufactured pieces. Conversely, older pieces have an apparently endless market, especially so if the item is more unusual and appeals to collectors. Thus, much of this book has concentrated on the more obscure forms of fossil resin used for the production of jewellery.

Very little amber comes on to the market today in an unadulterated form. The majority of amber from northern Europe has been heated, clarified and often subjected to various block-pressing processes so that it can be manufactured easily into beads of uniform colour and composition. Thus, most of the clear amber offered for sale is of a deep syrup colour, that is much deeper than would be the case if the pieces had simply been cleaned from their natural state and then worked. On top of this, from the 1950s came the vogue for sun-spangle inclusions, which in reality were a by-product of the amber being cooled too quickly once clarified, thus setting off internal stresses which appear as discoidal rings (*Figure 6.10*). When they first became popular, nature was even further enhanced by these stress rings being dyed red or green. The effect is very curious, and the fashion did not last long.

Figure 6.10 Stress ring inclusions. *Courtesy of Peter Read.*

Even the stress ring has now been manufactured in plastic jewellery – usually that originating from Germany – and sometimes these rings do not have the radiating lines but are simply flat, hollow discs.

The clear amber is either simply cut into square blocks and polished into cubes for necklaces – this being especially the case with pressed amber – or it is moulded into beads. Pressed amber is manufactured in such quantities today that much of it can be recognized on sight as it has a slipshod finish and the internal structure is dirty, the various constituents not being properly mixed. This characteristic should not be confused with the natural swirl marks found in some Dominican amber. Much of the pressed amber is produced in Germany and Poland. Surprisingly, foreign outlets for Russian shops carry some stock that is natural amber, as well as the cloudy, custard-coloured beads from such manufacturers as Almazjuvelirexport, Moscow. This latter may well be a matter of foreign currency and costs. Certainly within Eastern Europe, in countries like Hungary, only the manufactured amber is available, while in Western Europe the range of ambers is much more extensive, with the emphasis on natural resin.

The threat to produce counterfeit amber comes from Germany where more money is available and the market is larger and thus there is more temptation. The processes involved are very simple in comparison to the production of gem crystals, and one has to be consistently on the look-out for new variations. In late 1985, the author was alerted by a jeweller that some pendants, purchased from a reputable German dealer, had turned out to be colourless in the interior once worked. Samples were sent to the London Gem Testing Laboratory and surprisingly turned out not to be as first thought, plastic coated with natural resin, but 'amber' which had been made colourless (presumably by overheating) and then oxidized. The latter process of course had only affected the surface. Comparisons were made in the USA and many items – necklaces, pendants, etc. – were found that had been subjected to the same process. It has been decided to term this product 'surface colour-treated amber' by the Gemological Institute of America (GIA) and the Gem Testing Laboratory in London (*see Plate 8f*).

With the entry of China into Western commerce, and the appearance of 'Chinese amber' of a clear deep-coloured tone, usually sold as cabochons or small round beads, many doubts were expressed as to the origin of this product as well. However, as can be seen from the infra-red spectrograms in Appendix 3, this is certainly not clarified succinite as the reading is quite different. Perhaps it is from Fushun coalfield.

One product which may well originate in China or Hongkong, and which has so far not been seen in Britain but has appeared in Rome, is a range of fine, clear golden amber carvings, moulded but hand-finished. These works, about 7 to 10 cm high, usually depict animals or birds, but the giveaway sign is the insertion of what appears to be green fern-like plant matter, which is made to coil inside the carving. Also, on close inspection there is often a bubble that has broken the surface in some inconspicuous spot but has not been noticed in the manufacturing process, and has thus been left unaltered.

Lastly, I am often asked about restoration and conservation of amber objects. The two processes are very different; the former including the addition of melted, colour-blended material with the hope to deceive and achieve a higher sale price, the latter undertaken with the premise that all work should be able to be dismounted at a future occasion when perhaps even better forms of conservation become available (*Figure 6.11*).

Restoration and conservation are the two areas of passing on information about amber where I am most hesitant. My advice is only to wait. At the moment there is no universal agreement as to how amber should be conserved to stop oxidation. Various museums employ different methods, depending on whether the object is a specimen for study purposes, in which case light oils or even water might be used for storage purposes, or for show purposes, where a surface covering is usually given, and attempts are made to ensure that the objects are not placed under lighting which also gives off heat. Much work is being carried out on conservation and restoration of resins, and it is hoped that within the next five years the picture will be much clearer.

The following is an extract from a paper given by Beck, C. W. (1982) at the Washington Congress for Science and Technology in the Service of Conservation.

'It has long been known that the principal danger to amber objects is oxidation by atmospheric oxygen; light and heat appear to be relevant only insofar as they accelerate this

Figure 6.11 Small casket, badly damaged.

oxidation. The effects of air on amber include darkening, loss of polish, and a craquelure that will eventually lead to deep cracks and render the object opaque and brittle.

The earliest means of protecting amber from air is immersion in water to which various preservatives have been added to prevent fouling. Helm used as much as 15–20% ethanol; this amount was later reduced to about 1% but Klebs and Langerken warn that *any* amount of ethanol will render amber porous and opaque on long exposure. The same would apply to the addition of ether. Formaldehyde was first used at concentrations of 4%; these were later reduced to 0.5–1.5%, but according to La Baume even these are deleterious to amber. Additions of unspecified amounts of glycerol, of 5% sodium chloride or of traces of camphor have been recommended and seem to be innocuous. Immersion of amber objects in pure paraffin oil is mentioned. Klebs describes the preservation of amber inclusions in airtight glass-covered boxes. This is obviously safe and aesthetically much superior to immersion in liquids. Exhibition cases filled with nitrogen would constitute a perfect environment for valuable amber carvings in the modern museum.

Amber surfaces have been protected by coating them with mixtures of gelatin and glycerol, but the coating becomes opaque in a few years when it must be removed with warm water and renewed. Botfeldt rightly considers this method unsuitable. A great many natural and synthetic materials have been and are still being used for coating amber finds, including xylene solutions of Canada balsam, turpentine solutions of damar, amber varnish, shellac, zapon lacquer (cellulose nitrate), Mowilith 30 and 35/73, poly(vinyl chloride), celluloid, and poly(butyl methacrylate).

Amber inclusions must be cut and polished for microscopic examination; to preserve them for future study, they are often embedded in mixtures of damar and turpentine between microscope slides.

Repairs to Baltic amber objects may be made by moistening the fracture surfaces with aqueous potassium hydroxide and pressing the fragments together, a procedure that is also presented as a test for authenticity because it fails with amber imitations. Celluloid and alcoholic solutions of amber or of rosin are mentioned for cementing amber.

Any conservation treatment with natural or synthetic materials will introduce into an amber object contaminants that must interfere with its future authentication or provenience analysis. When some sort of treatment is absolutely necessary to prevent the decomposition of an amber find, paraffin is the only substance that can be used with safety . . . It is unique in that it does not absorb radiation in the principal diagnostic region of provenience analysis by infrared spectroscopy.'

Bibliography

BAUER, M., *Precious Stones*, Charles Griffin, London (1904)

BECK, C. W., Authentication and conservation of Amber: Conflict of Interests, Washington Congress for Science and Technology in the Service of Conservation (1982).

BECK, C. W., GERVING, M. AND WILBUR, E., 'The provenience of archaeological amber artifacts, parts I and II', *Art and Archaeology Technical Abstracts*, supplement (1966, 1967)

HANAUSEK, E., 'Das Färben des Bernsteins', *Industrie Blätter* **21**, 37 (1884)

KLEBS, R., 'Uber Farbe und Imitation des Bernsteins', *Schriften der Phys. Okon. Ges. Königsberg*, **28** (1887)

KUNZ, G. F., *The Curious Lore of Precious Stones*, reprinted by Dover Publications, New York (1971)

READ, C., *Transactions of the Norfolk and Norwich Naturalist's Society*, Vol (iii) (1884)

REES, A., *The Cyclopaedia of Arts, Sciences and Literature*, Vol. XXIV, Longman, London (1819)

WILLIAMSON, G., *The Book of Amber*, Ernest Benn, London (1932)

Chapter 7

Composition and plastics

The use of the term *plastics*, for a range of products that could be shaped when hot and plastic into articles and components, came into use around 1920. Before then, the available products of this sort were known as *composition*. This term included products made from pitch, bitumen, rosin, copal, shellac, celluloid, casein and the early phenolic resins (primarily Bakelite). Frequently, reinforcing fillers, including wood, flour, asbestos and limestone powder, were compounded in.

These early synthetics were not used in the imitation of amber but more for jet, ivory, horn and tortoiseshell. Important nineteenth-century breakthroughs include Hancock's prototype of a mill to process rubber (1820) and Charles Goodyear's production of vulcanite rubber (1838).

Today there are over 60 products in common use that could be termed composition or plastic, and we have come to accept trade names like Bakelite or Perspex as part of day-to-day vocabulary. Time passes – who would have thought that Tupperware (polyethylene) parties would have been taking place since 1946 – and now within the sphere of amber imitation, we not only have plastic *per se* but also combination products of plastic plus natural amber chips or dust, that add further to the confusion.

There are so many manufactured synthetic materials used in place of amber that the gemmologist, as analyst, needs a knowledge of basic molecular chemistry as well as the usual mineralogy when dealing with organic gem materials. This has come, in part, from a new enthusiasm for collecting synthetics in their own right, resulting in the customer expecting an analysis beyond the generic term 'plastic' with regard to identification, and also from the ceaseless vigilance necessary to spot new gemstone imitations as soon as they appear on the market.

The following are basic 'thumb-nail sketches' of the various types of plastics that are likely to be confused with natural fossil resin. As well as the history of each plastic, included so the gemmologist can ascertain the earliest possible date for a given object, the characteristics are shown for identification purposes. The usual method of analysis of such non-ambers is to take a specific gravity test (fossil resin has a lower specific gravity than almost all plastics commonly used in imitation), and to burn a shaving from an inconspicuous part of the object. (*See* end of chapter for test details.)

Cellulose nitrate

In 1835 Pelouse nitrated cellulose, and in 1840 Alexander Parkes of Birmingham, England enlarged on this work by adding olive oil to nitro-cellulose (cellulose nitrate). Parkes called his product Parkesine, and today this is the most sought-after synthetic by the collector. The majority of pieces date from 1855, when the patent was granted, to 1868 when the company went into liquidation.

In 1870 the Hyatt brothers in America patented a product they called Celluloid, which differed from Parkesine in that camphor was added in place of olive oil. This was far more successful as a product and was produced extensively.

The drawback to Celluloid was that it was highly flammable, even explosive and thus, when considering amber substitutes, most unsuitable as a base for smoking requisites. It did, however, make an excellent substitute for ivory and tortoiseshell, and is still used today for piano keys and table tennis balls.

Characteristics of nitro-cellulose plastics

Thermoplastic
Refractive index: 1.495–1.51
Specific gravity: 1.36 (clear) to 1.80 (pigmented)
Readily sectile under knife; cuts with smooth sliver. Peelings burn easily, explode and pop inside a test tube when heated. Burns with a yellow flame. On gentle heating, Celluloid exudes a smell of camphor and this can sometimes be detected by rubbing the sample vigorously. Softens with acetone.

Cellulose acetate (safety Celluloid)

Cross and Bevan invented a process for cellulose acetate in 1894, but it was not until Eichengrün produced a cellulose acetate moulding material, in about 1930, that injection-moulded cellulose acetate began to appear.

Patent example of the period

1920:   Lindsay, W. G. Amber substitutes. Imitation made from acetyl cellulose (cellulose acetate). Patent 1 319 229 (USA).

Cellulose acetate, being of low flammability, was used extensively for toys, hair combs, spectacle frames, etc. Katz (1984) records over 70 trade names.

Characteristics of cellulose acetate plastics

Thermoplastic
Refractive index: 1.490–1.505
Specific gravity: 1.3 (clear) to 1.8 (pigmented)
Under knife sectile; cuts with a smooth sliver. Peelings smell of acetic acid (vinegar).
Very low flammability when flame-retardent plasticizer is present.

Casein

This was invented in 1890 by Spitteler and Krische in Germany, and patented in 1899
by them as Galalith (from the Greek words for milk and stone). In England it was
later called Erinoid as it was intended to manufacture the product from Irish milk.
The milk must be skimmed milk, with the fat removed, and this is precipitated with
rennet to form rennet casein. Far more casein (acid-precipitated) is used for glues and
distempers than for plastics.
    In the manufacture of casein plastic material, the rennet casein is ground and mixed
with water to form a gel, which is then extruded through a heated nozzle as rods or
tubes, hardened by soaking in dilute formaldehyde. Sheets are pressed from the rods,
and it has been machined since 1914, for example in button making. Both Galalith
and Erinoid were made commonly before the First World War.
    Although the most common casein imitations were for 'horn' bangles and beads,
'amber' was also produced as can be gathered from the trade names such as Ambloid,
produced by Dai Nippon Celluloid Company of Osaka. Fifty-five trade names are
given in the 1934 *Directory of Plastics*.

Characteristics of casein

Thermoplastic
Refractive index: 1.54–1.56
Specific gravity: 1.32–1.39; usually 1.32–1.34
Under knife sectile; smooth slivers but tough. Blisters or dulls under a drop of nitric
acid. Chars readily; smells of burning protein (burnt milk or burnt feathers) when
heated in a flame.

Phenol formaldehyde resins

In 1859 Butlerow described formaldehyde polymers, and in 1899 Smith published a
patent on phenol formaldehyde composition. Then in 1907, James Swinburne, a Scot,
was beaten by only one day by Leo Baekeland, an American of Belgian origin, in
filing a patent for phenol formaldehyde resinous products.
    In about 1912, Baekeland introduced Bakelite moulding powders, which were used
as casings for wireless sets and as electrical insulating materials. These products
usually had dark brown or dull black fillers added to give flexibility. The publicity

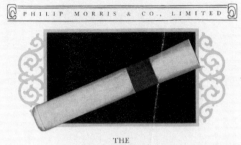

THE
"HALL" CIGARETTE TUBE

The "Hall" Tube is more than a handsome Amber and Gold Cigarette Holder. Its important feature is the screw joint in the gold band allowing for the insertion of an absorbent wad which filters the smoke, checks the passage of nicotine and tobacco dust, and keeps the tube sweet and clean. This tube recommends itself to doctors on the important ground of hygiene, while to the ordinary smoker it brings the pure unspoilt aroma of the cigarette right to the last draw.

As a gift to a cigarette-smoking friend, this handsome Amber and Gold Tube, in its neatly fitting case, is most attractive. The cloudy hand-cut amber is beautifully shaped and finished, while the gold band adds just the necessary touch of distinction that makes a present so acceptable and highly prized.

Prices:

AMBER

2¼" - 45/-		4½" - 100/-	
3 " - 54/-		5 " - 115/-	
3½" - 66/-		5½" - 140/-	
4 " - 84/-		6 " - 165/-	

VULCANITE

3 " - 35/-		5 " - 45/-	
3½" - 37/6		5½" - 47/6	
4 " - 40/-		6 " - 50/-	
4½" - 42/6			

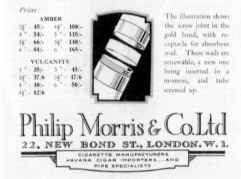

The illustration shows the screw joint in the gold band, with receptacle for absorbent wad. These wads are renewable, a new one being inserted in a moment, and tube screwed up.

Philip Morris & Co.Ltd
22, NEW BOND ST., LONDON.W.1.
CIGARETTE MANUFACTURERS
HAVANA CIGAR IMPORTERS ...AND
PIPE SPECIALISTS

Figure 7.1 Reproduction of an advertisement for the 'Hall' cigarette tube in amber and vulcanite.

granted to Bakelite was so extensive that today many other plastics are simply referred to erroneously as Bakelite.

Baekeland had actually been searching for an artificial substitute for shellac (brass bedsteads were in vogue as bedbugs could not bore into metal – unlike wood – and this was an ideal lacquer to prevent the need for constant polishing). It was some time before he found an application for the hard gem-like resin he had invented. He also faced opposition from Swinburne's Damard Lacquer Company (from 'damn hard lacquer' – not of French origin), and it was not until 1926 that Bakelite materials were strongly established in both the USA and Europe.

The production of phenol formaldehyde involves the reaction of phenol or cresol with formaldehyde in large, heated reaction vessels. Several varieties of phenol formaldehyde resin are made but the variety that is liable to feature as 'amber' is cast phenolic resin, made with a high formaldehyde content. It is made in clear transparent colours as well as opaque, and used for beads, bangles, drawer knobs, napkin rings, etc. It should be noted that phenolic resin yellows and darkens with age.

It is very tough and objects made out of it have often outlived the other parts of an assemblage.

According to Ellis (1923):

The production of amber-like products, according to Redman, Weith and Brock[30e] is carried out by first forming an initial product from phenol and formaldehyde without the addition of any condensing agent. Thus 3 parts of a 40 per cent solution of formaldehyde and 5 parts of phenol are boiled at atmospheric pressure for a period ranging from 60 to 120 hours. A viscous creamy lower layer forms and a supernatant layer of water which is practically free from formaldehyde. Cresol does not require boiling for so long a period, ordinary commercial cresol reacting sufficiently in from 4 to 12 hours and when crude cresol is used the period may be shortened to about 2 hours. With pure phenol the reaction may be accelerated by heating under pressure to 125°C. In this case the time of heating will range from 12 to 18 hours. After a viscous resinous mass is obtained in this manner 2 parts additional of formaldehyde, that is two-thirds of the amount of formaldehyde originally employed, is stirred into the first reaction product (the water which separated in the first stage having previously been removed). The formaldehyde is added at a temperature of about 100°C. and the mixture allowed to cool to 60–70°C. Then heat is applied and water is evaporated rapidly, the temperature rising to about 115°C. Some formaldehyde will escape during this operation. Ordinarily the concentration is carried to a point which renders the mix quite viscous but still permits pouring. Boiling should be stopped before the material reaches a gelatinous state. After concentration 3 to 5 per cent of formaldehyde is added to replace loss occurring during concentration and the material is poured into molds. It is allowed to set at a temperature of 50–100°C. When sufficiently firm it is removed from the molds and kept at the same temperature for a period of several weeks or several months, depending on the thickness of the molded masses. By mildly heating the material for a protracted period as described, an amber-like product is obtained which is used to make pipe stems, cigar holders and similar articles. A finer color may be obtained and a harder product which may be machined, sandpapered and buffed to better advantage by exposing the material to a finishing heat of 125°C. or even higher for a period of several days. The color may be varied by introducing dyes such as auramin to produce a deep amber colour or methyl violet to yield an amethyst color. The addition of oils or waxes in small quantity yields an opaque material. Ground mica or fish-scales may be used to produce a shimmering effect.

Baekeland[30f] prepares amber-like products by heating phenol and hexamethylenetetramine, with or without the presence of water, to form hard, infusible resins containing free ammonia.

[30e] J. S. C. I. 1919, 647A; U. S. Pats. 1,310,087 and 1,310,088, July 15, 1919; 1,374,526, Apr. 12, 1921.

[30f] U. S. Pat. 1,187,230, June 13, 1916.

Amber Substitutes

'Amber-like substances such as are used in pipe stems and for other purposes, made from resorcinol heated with formaldehyde, have been produced by Peter.[76]

[76] J. S. C. I. 1915, 914; U. S. Pat. 1,147,264. Farugi and Cioni, Boll. Chim. Farm. 1919, *58*, 101; J. S. C. I. 1919, 427A, have described the irritation of the mucous membrane caused by the use of some imitation amber mouth-pieces. This they attribute to the freeing of formaldehyde from a casein compound by action of smoke and saliva. Sachs, Wiener klin. Wochschr., 1921, *34*, 356, states that the manufacture of artificial amber (bakelite is specified) in Austria has led to increasing numbers of cases of dermatitis directly due to exposure to the fumes of phenol, formaldehyde and ammonia in the plants. He describes suitable therapeutic measures and urges proper protection for the workers.

Cast phenolic resin

In 1928 the Catalin Corporation (USA) produced a phenolic resin of high formaldehyde ratio and this enabled a phenolic resin syrup to be cast in a mould and cured by oven heating. This process did not reach Britain until 1937. These dates are important as the casting process offered the opportunity for the first time for the production of a transparent, tough phenolic resin. It is from *cast* phenolic resin that most pre-Second World War imitation amber objects and items of jewellery are made.

Cast phenolics are produced in transparent, opaque and variegated colours. Most of the amber-like cast phenolics are clear cherry-red, opaque rust-red, opaque gold or yellow – even opaque green was fashionable for a time. This latter is somewhat of a glorification of nature's own product which is extremely rare; thus any green amber item should be regarded with extreme caution. *Figure 7.2* illustrates items made from cast phenolic resin.

Figure 7.2 Umbrella handles in cast phenolic resin.

The peak for amber as a colour appears to have been between 1930 and 1935, and during this time it appears in wireless casings, writing sets, table lamp stands and all manner of objets d'art. The more popular opaque tone was produced by additives.

Many small items, including pipe stems, cigar or cigarette holders and beads, were machined from large blocks. Bangles were made from cast rod.

Characteristics of cast phenolic resins

Thermosetting
Refractive index: 1.54–1.70; usually 1.63–1.66
Specific gravity: 1.25–2.00 (appreciably higher than natural amber)

Under knife sectile; tough, powdery chips. Burns but extinguishes itself when flame removed. Burns with a strong smell of phenol (carbolic acid). This smell can sometimes be released when the item is wet or warmed.

Amino-formaldehyde resins and plastics: urea formaldehyde moulding materials

In 1884 Hölzer isolated urea formaldehyde condensation products, and in 1918 John patented 'Urea formaldehyde condensating resin'. Commercial production of moulding materials made from urea formaldehyde resin and cellulose filler started in 1928.

The prime objective was to make a water-white colourless casting resin, but this was not achieved. Moulding powders are, however available in a range of pale translucent and opaque colours: the objects are produced from moulds in heated hydraulic presses, the curing time being only a number of minutes. One of the most popular uses for urea formaldehyde materials was for the early production of picnic ware. One trade name was Birmite, which should not be confused with the Burmese natural resin 'burmite'.

Characteristics of urea formaldehyde moulding materials

Thermosetting
Refractive index: 1.54–1.56
Specific gravity: 1.45–1.55, usually about 1.50
Under knife sectile, with powdery chips, tough. Burns with a fishy smell, and formaldehyde and ammonia. Chars when heated in flame.

Recent plastics

The early plastics all had specific gravities higher than natural resins, and could therefore be separated by a specific gravity test involving a brine solution: 10 level teaspoonfuls of salt to 250 ml of water will suffice. Necklaces and other large items can be tested in this way without much difficulty, providing the item is washed afterwards to remove the saline crust which would otherwise develop. Care must however be taken with modern plastics as polystyrene has a specific gravity lower than natural resins. It is unlikely that a gemmologist would suspect a polystyrene item of being fossil resin, but when fillers are used the resultant mass could cause confusion. A burnt shaving test is therefore recommended if, after the brine test, the item is still giving cause for concern.

Polystyrene

Plastics based on styrene became available shortly before the Second World War from the Dow Chemical Company in the USA and IG Farben in Germany. They caused particular interest because of good electrical insulation characteristics, and were an essential component of radar. During the war, the US Government also initiated a crash programme for the installation of plants for the manufacture of a rubber from butadiene and styrene. After hostilities ceased, this left a large surplus capacity of plant for the manufacturer of styrene and polystyrene, and it was therefore found possible to produce polystyrene, not as an expensive electrical insulator but as a cheap, general-purpose thermoplastic.

Styrene is produced by dehydrogenation of ethyl benzene. Trade names include Distrine (British Resin Products Ltd) and Erinoid Polystyrene (Mobil Chemicals Ltd).

Characteristics of polystyrene

Thermoplastic
Refractive index: 1.59–1.67
Specific gravity: 1.05–1.07 (will float with amber in saline solution)
Hardness: $2\frac{1}{4}$–$2\frac{1}{2}$
Dissolves in organic hydrocarbon liquids such as benzene, bromoform and methylene iodide. Sectile. Softens at 70–90°C.

Polymethyl methacrylate (PMMA)

Technically the most important acrylic-type resins are methyl methacrylate polymers known variously as Perspex, Diakon, Plexiglas, etc. Perspex was developed commercially shortly before the Second World War by ICI in Britain.

The acrylate and methacrylate polymers differ widely in physical properties: methyl acrylate polymer is soft and somewhat rubber-like whereas methyl methacrylate polymer is hard.

Characteristics of polymethyl methacrylate

Thermoplastic
Refractive index: 1.50
Specific gravity: 1.18–1.19
Hardness: 2
Attacked by acetone. Burns with fruity or floral odour and a bluish flame. False teeth are made from PMMA.

Slocum imitation amber

This is produced by Slocum Laboratories, Royal Oak, Michigan, USA (Rice, 1980). This substance is not known in Britain but it is understood to be a plastic which burns with a fruity odour, and may well therefore be an acrylic resin. The GIA give constants as:

Refractive index: 1.50–1.55
Specific gravity: 1.17 mean

It occurs as a dark 'cooked' resin complete with many induced stress rings. Slocum opal is familiar in Britain: this has a glass base.

Thermosetting ethenoid plastics

Polyester

In 1847 Berzelins made the first polyester, and thermosetting ethenoid plastics were introduced commercially during the Second World War (1941) in the USA, later rising to importance as glass-reinforced polyester – better known as GRP. The production involves complex ester compounds which are thermosetting and can be polymerized at room temperature.

As the plastic can be both hot or cold-cured, it has a huge application in the model and craft market. Polyester resin is frequently used for embedding specimens of natural history in the classroom, and finds a ready sale in souvenir shops in the form of paperweights. On a more serious note, genuine inclusions in rare ambers are sometimes embedded in polyester resin for preservation purposes:

'To overcome the unfavourable characteristics of the resin (Cenomanian period in France) the preparation of the Arthropods took the following course: Inspection under water with a binocular microscope; wet grinding; embedding in polyester resin; grinding and polishing of the Arthropod-containing resin fragment in its polyester mantle to obtain an oriented surface. (Schlüter, 1978)

Commercial embedding process

Dried specimens (usually insects in the case of spurious amber) are injected with liquid resin if the body cavity is of some size, to prevent unwanted trapped air bubbles, and the object is then dyed if this is considered necessary, with a spirit-soluble stain.

If the specimen is very small it may be sprayed with lacquer to give it more strength, and any broken part can be adjoined with epoxy resin.

Water-clear polyester resin can be tinted by the addition of transparent colouring dye stuff and a ratio of 2% catalyst. Moulds are usually of wax-coated glass or aluminium.

Polybern

An embedding process with polyester resin has been explained as this is used in the production of articles termed Polybern. By this means, small chips of amber in polyester resin are cast as a mosaic. Polybern first appeared in moulded or cast vases from Poland, but is now in wider production within the Eastern Bloc and Germany. This is a particularly unattractive product, and of course the constants are variable as the relative proportions vary.

TABLE 7.1 Tests for natural amber, copal and plastic imitations

Material	Specific gravity	Refractive index	On burning, shaving or similar	Under knife	Other useful data
Natural amber	1.08 (mean)	1.54 (mean)	Slightly aromatic. Subtle depending on when worked	Splinters except under newly sharpened blade	Learn to develop 'eye'; compare with actual example at all times
Copal	1.06	1.53	Very aromatic. Can stick in threads to needle	Splinters	Softens under ethyl alcohol. Leave drop on surface one minute; will then take imprint of finger, etc. Also releases aromatic smell when rubbed vigorously. Crazing is quite different from amber
Blond tortoiseshell	1.29	1.53	Smells like burnt hair	Sectile	
Cellulose nitrate	1.37–1.43*	1.49–1.52	Smells like camphor. May burn explosively	Sectile	Soluble in ether – amber not affected by short immersion
Cellulose acetate	1.29–1.35	1.49–1.51		Sectile	Thermoplastic
Casein	1.32–1.43	1.49–1.54	Smells like burnt milk	Sectile	Is *not* electrostatic
Phenol formaldehyde resin	1.26–1.28	1.64–1.66	Smells acrid	Sectile	Chars black, does not burn
Urea formaldehyde resin	1.48–1.55	1.55–1.62		Sectile	
Polymethyl methacrylate (Perspex or Diakon)	1.18–1.19	1.50	Smells like burnt fruit	Sectile	
Polystyrenes (Distrine or Trolutol)	1.05	1.58–1.67		Sectile	Soluble in benzene or toluene; softens at 70–90°C
Polyester	1.23	1.49–1.51		Sectile	

*Figures vary considerably depending on fillers used.

Bernat/Bernit

This is produced from Polyester resin by Gebhardt Wilhelm in Germany. It contains stress-induced rings, and according to Rice (1980), the discoidal stress spangles are circular but lack the radiating lines of stress rings within natural amber. It is also found with implanted inclusions.

This type of non-radiating stress ring amber is encountered in Britain in costume jewellery. Most of the necklaces are composed of different coloured plastic beads, only some of which mimic amber. They are said to come from Germany and retail in 1986 for about £20, new.

Characteristics of Bernat

Refractive index: 1.49–1.51
Specific gravity: 1.23 mean

Epoxy (epoxide) resins

Epoxy resins are made by reacting epichlorhydrin with diphenylol propane or a hydroxy-containing phenol formaldehyde resin. This becomes thermoset when heated with cross-linking reagents. The first patent on epoxides was taken out in Germany in 1939.

Epoxy resins are used with phenolic resins in coating surfaces to confer a tougher exterior to softer recent resins like copal, or to increase the strength of melted ambers in industrial applications. Cast epoxide did not appear commercially until 1955.

1957:   Rozhdesterniskii, V. A., Petrov, G. S. and Serganova, G. L. Increasing the thermal stability, light resistance and mechanical strength of amber. The properties are improved by fusing or mixing in a common solvent, with 2 – 5% of its own weight of epoxy resin. Patent 105 899 (USSR).

These are the most difficult of all adulterations to spot, and if any 'amber' gives unusual readings on testing, it is always worth taking a peeling, and also examining the specimen under a low-power microscope. When epoxide resin is used as a coating, junction marks are usually evident under the microscope but may take some time to locate. Epoxide has a sharp, acrid odour and burns with black smoke.

Bibliography

ELLIS, C., *Synthetic Resins and their Plastics*, Chemical Catalog Company, New York (1923)

KATZ, S., *Plastics: Design and Materials*, Studio Vista, London (1978)

KATZ, S., *Classic Plastics*, Studio Vista, London (1984)

KAUFMAN, M., *The First Century of Plastics*, Plastics Institute, London (1963)

REDFARN, C. A., *A Guide to Plastics*, London (1958)

RICE, P. C., *Amber, the Golden Gem of the Ages*, Van Nostrand Reinhold, New York (1980)

SCHLÜTER, T., 'Zur Systematik und Palökologie harzkonservierter Arthropoda einer Taphozönose aus dem Cenomanium von NW-Frankreich', *Berliner Geowissenschaftliche Abhandlungen*, (9), Verlag von Dietrich Reimer, Berlin (1978)

SUTERMEISTER, E. and BROWNE, F. L., *Casein and its Industrial Application*, New York (1939)

YARSLEY, V. E. and COZENS, E. G., *Plastics*. Also: *Plastics in the Service of Man*, Penguin, London (1945)

Chapter 8

Amber from Asia

'When a tiger dies, its soul penetrates the earth, and is a stone. This object resembles amber, and is therefore called hu'po (Tiger's soul).' (*Pen ts'as Kang mu*, Li Shih Chen, sixteenth century)

History

Although most gemmologists associate the Orient with Burmese amber – named burmite by Otto Helm – it is to Chinese writings that we have to look for early references to this substance.

Amber is not mentioned in classical Chinese texts but it is written in a very early Chinese manuscript, *The Annals of the Former Han Dynasty* (Pan Ku and Pan Chao), that Ki Pin (Kashmire) produces amber. While this is unlikely to be geologically correct, Kashmir may well have been a staging post for some distant resin, perhaps from Syria, and relations between China and Kashmir were certainly cordial during the reigns of the Emperors Wu and Ch'eng in the first century BC.

A century later Pliny, in his *Historia Naturalis*, quotes Indian amber in three passages:

(1) From the statement of Nicias that amber is found in India where it is held as a preferable substitute for frankincense.
(2) After Ctesias, that there is in India a river called Hypobarus; that this river discharges near a mountain covered with trees which produce electrum; and that these trees are called *siptachorae* (intense sweetness).
(3) Archelaus, who reigned over Cappadocia (under the Roman Emporer Tiberius), says that it is brought from the country in a rough state, and with the fine bark still adhering to it, 'owing to its transparency, certain objects are seen within, ants for example, gnats and lizards'.

These references would all seem to be to modern resins, and not amber.

What is of more interest is that on two occasions in the Chinese record, amber from Syria appears to have been in use in the Roman Empire.

In *The Annals of the Later Han Dynasty*, it is recorded that Ai Lao (the ancient name for the Shan Kingdom) produces lustrous pearls* and amber. This kingdom, established in the first century AD, embraced nearly the whole of Yunnan as well as part of Tonkin and Kwang-si.

The trade route from what is now Burma through Yunnan Province into Central China has been established for so long that amber is usually, erroneously presumed by Chinese writers to originate in Yunnan. However, the ancient Chinese word for amber, *Tun Mou* (rather than *Hu P'o*), probably relates to a Shan language rather than a Chinese one:

'Tun mou picks up mustard seeds tun mou is identical with hu-p'o'. (Wang Ch'ung; AD 27–97)

Amber is included in a third-century dictionary, the *Kuang Ya* of AD 227–240. The description is again somewhat confusing but so early a reference is worth citing:

'Amber is a pearl. Above it and beside it, no plants grow. The least depth (at which it occurs in the soil) amounts to [1.5 metres], the greatest depth is from [2.4 to 2.7 m]. It is as big as hu [a measure holding 90 litres]. By cutting off the rind, the amber is obtained. At first it is like the gum of a peach tree but being stiffened and hardened it assumes form. The people living in the district work it into head pillows. It is produced by Po Nan hsein [Yung Ch'ang in Yunnan].'

The reference to 'pearl' may relate to the fact that amber is used as a bead. This linguistic interchange arises in several European languages as well. Amber from Yung Ch'ang is also included in a medical work of the same period, the *Pieh lu*, so the Chinese also used amber medicinally from an early date.

Ta'o Hung-Ching (AD 452–536) remarks:

'There is an old saying that the resin of fir trees sinks into the earth, and transforms itself after a thousand years. When it is burned it still has the odour of fir trees. There is also amber, in the midst of which there is a single bee, in shape and colour like a living one (see below). There is also amber made by boiling chicken-eggs with the roe of the dark fish, but this is not genuine. Only the kind which when rubbed in the palm of the hand, and made warm, attracts mustard seeds is genuine.'

'Resin after a thousand years makes Fu Ling, after a thousand years makes amber, after a thousand years makes gall stone, after a thousand years makes wei hsi [sublime happiness].' (Wang Ts'e-ching)

In other writings, *hsi* is given as *jet*, e.g. *Su King*, seventh century. Jet seems to have been imported from Turkistan from the fifth to the twelfth centuries AD.

There is an ancient Chinese legend that in the sand of Nin chou (Yunnan) there are cliffs full of bees. When the cliffs collapse, the bees come out of the earth and the people burn them or make them into amber.

The Chinese distinguished several types of amber:

---

*Freshwater pearls, as oyster pearls are recorded separately.

'Red fir tree resin, stone amber, water amber, flower amber, amber "of objects and figures", black amber [hsi or jet], and amber proper [hu p'o]. Amongst these red fir-tree resin is like amber, except that it is dull, in large pieces and brittle, with streaks extending cross-wise. As regarding water amber, there are many pieces that are not red, but rather light in tinge; among those which are yellow, there are many with furrowed stripes. Stone amber is heavy like stone, yellow in colour, but not fit for use. Flower amber resembles "new horse tails" [discoidal inclusions?] and the inner part of a pine tree. It has streaks alternately red and yellow. ,
   Amber of object and figures contains objects in its interior. Jet amber is the most excellent of the figure ambers. The amber proper is blood-red in colour.' (Lei Hsiao, author of *P'ao Chi lun*, a fifth-century pharmacopoeia)

We do not know from the above which types of amber came from Burma, but during our early Medieval period additional sources of amber opened up to the Chinese from both East and West.

Tributes of amber are recorded from Japan and also from Turkish tribes:

   9 catties of amber and 20 pieces of large amber (AD 951)
  50 catties of amber (AD 951)
 500 catties of amber (AD 965)

There are two extraordinary thirteenth-century references to amber which show that extensive trade had developed, but the origin of this distant resin was still not known. In the first, amber is mentioned among the products of the West brought to Sumatra, for trans-shipment to the Chinese port of Ch'uan chou fu. It is stated to have come from Arabia (Chao ju-kua). In the second, a Persian book of the same period, the *Jami ul hikayat*, remarks of the Chinese: 'All sorts of textiles are found with them, some of which are brought to Khorassan, with marvellous curiosities. Their merchandise consists of resin, incense, and yellow amber coming from the country of the slavs. This is a resin thrown out by the sea of the slavs.'

By the seventeenth and eighteenth centuries amber was imported from many sources. The Dutch of the seventeenth century imported amber into Formosa among some other articles of trade for further export to China, but nothing seems to be known about the origin of this amber (Reiss). In Macao the Portugese exported ivory, amber, coarse and fine woollen cloths, and were reported to handle amber of both the gold and water type (*Gazetteer of the Province of Kuangtung and Ao Men chi lio*).

Of the native Asian amber, the Portuguese Jesuit Father Alvarez Semedo, who arrived in China in 1613, wrote:

'Yunnan is a great countrie, but hath little merchandise. I know not any thing that is brought from thence, unless it bee that matter, whereof they make the beads for chapplets, which the Portugal they call Alambras, and in Castile, Ambares, and are like amber, they are counted good against Catarre. It is digged out of mines, and sometimes in great pieces, it is redder than our amber, but not so cleane.' (Semedo, 1655)

The Dutchman Father Du Halde (1738) wrote a century later of amber from Yunnan: 'It produces red amber, but no yellow. Some think that rubies and other precious stones are brought hither from the Kingdom of Ava.'

The first Europeans to visit the site of the amber mines in Burma were Captain Hannay in 1836 and Dr Griffiths in 1837. Prior to this time the Chinese had been virtually the sole visitors, trading with the amber district or purchasing their supplies at Bhamo (Yule, 1858).

Noetling, who carried out a thorough geological examination of the amber mines in 1891, confirmed the trade route (Noetling, 1892): 'By far the large proportion of raw burmite is brought by Chinese traders and transported on the route north of Mogoung via Myitkyina into Yunnan'. The centre of the Burmese amber industry is the village of Maingkhwan inhabited by the Shan tribes, in the district of Myitkyina, which is only about 110 English miles from the city of Yung Ch'ang in Yunnan. The samples from Noetling's trip were later analysed in Danzig by Otto Helm, who subsequently gave the name of the resin from Burma as burmite.

Owing to political disturbances, the trade between Yunnan and Myitkyina seems to have gradually decreased in the late nineteenth century, and local direct trade sprang up with Mandalay and Rangoon.

Meanwhile amber from both Japan and Europe continued to enter China, this time via the ports of Shanghai and Canton, and the *Reports of the Chinese Maritime Customs* make interesting reading. Laufer (1907) concluded: 'even in Mandalay the succinite, or Prussian amber, is now easier to procure and cheaper, than the Burmese amber'. The amber workers themselves apparently stated that Indian amber (the local term for imported succinite) was more satisfactory to work, the fissures and cracks of burmite being a serious drawback.

Laufer also noted that 'the amber now used in Korea comes exclusively from Germany. The import from Germany amounts to:

1898: 11 498 yen
1899:   510 yen
1900: 2 111 yen
1901: 5 280 yen'.

Burma

It can be seen from the previous section that although Baltic amber was traded to China and Burma over many centuries, the major Asian amber of commerce was burmite.

Colour and size of burmite

Burmite ranges from a dark, rich brown (known to Indian gemmologists as horse-hoof), through to a watery, pale sherry. It is never bright, saffron-yellow or osseous like Baltic amber; however, occasionally it does present itself in a mottled coffee and cream combination due to the presence of calcite in the resin. This root amber is especially popular with Oriental lapidaries. The most famous and sought-after colour tone encountered with burmite is a bright, cherry-red. This does occur quite naturally, and referring back to ancient texts seems to have been the original Tiger's Soul, but dyed ambers and even plastics have been used extensively to mimic this rare amber; therefore any object which is of this colour should be regarded with grave suspicion.

Burmite has been found in surprisingly large agglomerations. These large masses appear to be similar to solid petroleum and present a remarkable visual similarity to the large masses of amber from the Dominican Republic.

Burmite is said to fluoresce in daylight conditions in the usual range of green-blue or purple. This is undoubtedly true as it has been noted in so many early sources but it is possibly due to the alteration of the resin once exposed to atmospheric weathering (*see also* Chapters 9 and 11). Although the burmite might once have fluoresced, the author has been unable to observe this in the pieces she has handled to date.

Fluorescence, like everything else, has been subject to the vagaries of fashion and it is droll to read in a report of 1922: 'If the public [could be] persuaded to look upon fluorescence as a rarity rather than a blemish, it would certainly be worth while to exploit these [Burmese] mines thoroughly and scientifically' (Penzer, 1922).

Denny's manuscript contained the following: 'A necklace of large rounded graduated beads with a finely carved Buddha as a pendant belonging to Mr Leader Williams of Taormina is remarkable for its colouring, the whole necklace being a beautifully matched deep brown translucent amber with a bluish-purple fluorescence'.

Geology and trade routes

Burmite is of Eocene age, that is 38 to 54 million years old, and lies in Tertiary sediments of what is now Upper Burma. The series of shales, finely laminated sandstone and blue clays fills an old ocean gulf, and the pockets of amber within the blue clay are obviously of a secondary deposition. The upper surface of the clay has been turned brown through the oxidizing influence of the dense surface vegetation, and apparently amber found in this upper, brown layer is of poor quality, brittle and dried out.

Detailed geological exploration of the Hukawng Valley and Upper Chindwin was hampered historically by continued skirmishes among local tribes. Today, although the amber deposits are thought to be exhausted, a thorough scientific investigation is still lacking, this time because the area is a major focus for the illicit trafficking of narcotics, and the safety of such an expedition cannot be assured.

When one bears in mind the inaccessible location of these amber mines it is remarkable that the resin has been traded at all. This is especially the case as Burmese amber was not, as in other areas, gathered simply after flash-floods had dislodged it from its natural strata, but mined from narrow, frequently water-logged pits excavated in the jungle floor. How much more remarkable, then, that this resin was not only traded eastwards via Yunnan, or southwards in the nineteenth century via Mandalay and Rangoon but also, as early as 1795 Colonel Symes, the British Ambassador to the King of Ava, made his country aware of the resin when he received from the King 'a box containing amber, in large pieces, uncommonly pure'.

Geography of the mining area

The mines are situated in the north-west border division of Upper Burma (*Figure 8.1*) in the Chindwin District, and in the neighbourhood of Mainghkwan in the Hukawng

Figure 8.1 The amber district of Upper Burma.

Valley. The mines lie along the crest of a range of low hills, which rise abruptly to a height of about 45 m from the fertile valley of the Hukawng, stretching in a southerly direction from near Mainghwan for a distance of seven or eight miles to the village of Lalaung.

This ridge is so nearly level that it would appear to have once formed a terrace skirting the higher ranges. It is covered with dense, impenetrable vegetation. Exploitation of the amber commenced at the southern end near the village of Lalaung and proceeded north during the nineteenth and early twentieth centuries.

The mines

It is said that 'no principle or traditional rule guides the choice of a site, and that the finding of amber is entirely a matter of chance' (Stuart, 1923).

The only indication of the presence of pockets of amber is strings of coaly matter appearing in the clay. The usual method employed apparently was to sink a shaft into the clay, as near as possible to a spot where amber had been found previously or where a lucky find had already been recorded. If the pocket was too large to be worked out for one shaft, others were sunk as close as possible to it, and lateral galleries ran in any likely direction from the bottom.

The pits were generally only about $\frac{1}{3}$ metre square, just large enough for a single man to work in them; indeed, they were so narrow that the workmen often ascended or descended by placing their feet in holes made in the two sides of the pit walls. In many pits no sheeting was used as the soil was so stiff.

After working through 4 to 6 m of dry clay containing small pieces of lignite, there appeared a grey, slatey clay, and imperfectly formed lignite. At this layer the amber occurred in irregular pockets.

The following two accounts are written nearly a century apart, but they talk from first-hand experience of a remarkably unchanging scene.

Captain Hannay, recording for the *Journal of the Asiatic Society of Bengal*, wrote in 1837:

> 'The whole country presents a succession of small hills, the soil thereof consists of reddish or yellowish clay. The freshly dug earth has a very agreeable scent. The diggings are from 6 to 15 feet deep. Amber is found in large quantities. The deeper the digging the better the amber. The variety most esteemed which is of a brilliant pale yellow, can only be found it is stated at a depth of 40 feet.'

This would seem to be the same principle as the author found with Romanian amber. The surface deposits are richly coloured with browns, blacks, etc. while the amber found at some depth is pure, plain yellow.

Hannay also mentioned a second amber site, to the east of the Hukawng valley, called Kotah-bhum, but apparently the site was sacred to the local people and thus the amber could not be exploited.

Chibber, writing in *The Mineral Resources of Burma* (1934), noted that at that time there were 200 pits located three miles south of the village of Shingban, with other open pits nearby in Pangmamaw. The largest centre was south-west of Shingban where 150 miners worked in bamboo-lined pits. The coal seams and amber were encountered at 12 m with the water-table lying at 14.7 m. Various forms of mining were undertaken simultaneously. Thus at Wayutman 20 miners were engaged redigging old shafts and the amber was sluiced out during the wet season. At this later period Chibber records 500 or 600 abandoned pits in one area alone.

The miners

Captain Hannay mentions that during his visit to the mines in 1836, although the men were at work in ten pits, he did not see a piece of amber worth having. He adds, however, that they may have secreted the best pieces as he was 'accompanied by several Burmese officers'.

One year later, Griffith (1837) reported that there were only about a dozen men employed in the mines, which were then considered to be approaching exhaustion.

Noetling, while carrying out his geological survey of the mines in 1892, 'employed 12 coolies, dug 12 pits in a fortnight, but did not get enough amber to pay his men'. However, he saw large bags of burmite in the houses of Burmese cutters in Mandalay and concluded that the output in former times must have been greater, or that these quantities represented the accumulated production of 'scores of years'.

Penzer, writing in 1922, was not impressed: 'The amber diggers are an indolent and semi-civilized people, who only work in the mines as a change from their more congenial agricultural pursuits. They dig almost entirely on pure chance, and have no systematic way whatsoever of mining.'

Finally Chibber, writing in the 1930s, talks of the 'number of coolies', etc. and one is left with a feeling of frustration throughout about the vast cultural gap between the local people, who actually mined and worked the amber, and those who visited briefly from afar and made such condemning statements.

Annual output

Production, and the value of resin extracted, varied considerably each year (*Table 8.1*). This situation seems to have been exacerbated by inter-tribal fighting throughout the period in question.

TABLE 8.1 Annual production and value of burmite

| Year | Weight* | | Value (£) |
	lb (UK)	kg	
1897	1 568	710	
1904	300	136	
1905	14 112	6 410	945
1906	24 192	10 980	709
1907	4 928	2 237	
1908	5 488	2 492	
1913	1 120	510	
1914	1 456	660	
1915	1 288	585	
1916	620	280	
1917	6 619	3 000	
1918	325	150	
1919	829	380	
1920	8 064	3 660	1 666
1921	2 946	1 340	
1922	403	180	131
1926	3 950	1 790	
1927	7 050	3 200	
1928	2 940	1 330	
1929	1 959	889	
1930	207	94	

*All weights must be considered approximate, as figures are from various sources and have been subject to conversion so that valid comparisons can be made.

Oriental workmanship

Amber jewellery and objets d'art from the Far East tend to be categorized as 'Oriental' with no further subdivision. Separating those amber items made in Burma from those made in China is probably not too difficult but for some reason, possibly because of historic linguistic difficulties, little has been printed about Oriental ambers in Western texts.

The following must therefore be taken as merely an attempt to 'clear muddy waters' rather than as an authoritative designation of all Eastern ambers, and it is hoped that the simple classifications used will be a stepping-stone for others to pursue more detailed investigations.

Burma

The earliest items made locally with burmite appear to be cylindrical ear-plugs called *na-daungs* (*Figure 8.2*). It is written in the *T'ang shu* that the descendants of the Ai lao, the Nan chao, ornament their ears with pearls, green stone and amber.

Figure 8.2 Cylindrical ear-plugs (na-daung) in burmite.

The usage of these ear-cylinders was extremely protracted; Chibber recorded they were still being manufactured extensively in the 1930s. The plugs were about 2.5–3.8 cm in length, and 1.3–1.9 cm in diameter, being somewhat larger at the ends than in the middle. Hollow ear-tubes were also made of glass but the traditional materials of amber or gold maintained their supremacy.

The pattern varied somewhat from tribe to tribe: 'those worn by the Lapei, who inhabit the dense moist jungles to the North and East of Mogaung are of amber or silver from four to five inches in length' (Anderson, 1876).

The ceremony of piercing a child's ear was kept as a great ceremony in Burma. The lobe was punctured with needles of gold or silver, and the needles were moved once or twice a day until the edges of the wound healed. They were then withdrawn and the holes filled with small slips of bamboo, smooth round thin stalks of Nangye grass or the finer stems of elephant grass, after which the process of enlargement took place. This was gradual and took a long time; one additional stalk was added day by day, until the opening in the lobe was large enough to admit the full-sized ear-cylinder.

The custom of enlarging the lobe of the ear so as to enable it to carry ear-tubes appears to be an ancient custom and is supposed to be connected with sun-worship.

Spanish historians mention that elaborate religious ceremonies were held at the Temple of the Sun at Cuzco, on the occasion of the boring of the ears of young Peruvian nobles, and in Asia the image of the Gautama Buddha is always portrayed with long pendant ear lobes reaching to his shoulders.

In the late nineteenth century, when the majority of burmite went to Mandalay rather than through Yunnan to China, the resin was worked into mouthpieces for pipes, rosary beads, finger rings and trinkets – elephants, monkeys and fish were especially popular subjects. 'More elaborate and costly were figures of Gautama Buddha, but these have become vary scarce now [1892] as there are only two men living at present who understand the art of cutting such figures' (Noetling, 1892).

Frogs of amber or gilded metal were frequently worn as amulets by Burmese children to protect them from the evil eye, and in the early twentieth century uniform beads for Mandarin necklaces, ear-rings, bars for brooches, buttons and cufflinks were added to the list of products made in Mandalay and Rangoon, all obviously for export rather than for local use.

The process for working beads was apparently simple. The pieces were cut into rough cubes with a sharp knife (though it is more likely that they were abraded), the corners cut off and a hole drilled with flat-edged needles, fitted into a bamboo. The bead was then shaped with a file curved at the upper end and finally polished, first with a dried leaf which contained a considerable quantity of silica and then with petrified wood.

No account of Burmese amber would be complete without reference to two remarkable objects, once part of the Burmese regalia.

One is a magnificent duck (*Figure 8.3*) taken from the Mandalay Palace of King

Figure 8.3 Burmite Duck, once park of the Burmese Regalia from the Palace of King Theebaw.

Theebaw. The bird measures 28 cm in length and is about 15 cm wide. There are faint traces of gold-leaf decoration to emphasize the feathers, and the eye sockets, now empty, were probably set with rubies or some other gem.

The duck appears to have been carved from one single piece of dark brown burmite, with a little marbling present on the top of the tail (not to be confused with the light shadow of the photograph). The walls of the ducks are nearly 2 cm thick, and the two halves are hollowed out to make a vessel. There is very little crazing on the surface but the piece had been dropped and appears broken in several places. The construction of the piece is curious in that the upper portion is very finely carved, bold, decisive and flamboyant, while the under-section is crude, the blade marks of the knife still being visible on the supporting front and belly of the bird. Other similar birds, made of silver, accompanied this one as part of the regalia which was returned from London to Rangoon in 1964. However, the amber duck never reached Burma and its present whereabouts are not known.

The other object is a superb ball of clear red burmite, measuring about 10 cm in diameter, exhibited in 1924 among the Burmese exhibits at the British Empire Exhibition at Wembley. The description attached to it read:

'This amber ball is a historically authenticated Burmese antique, dating back to the Royal Burmese Dynasty prior to Kings Mindon Min and Theebaw, and was only used when one of the Chief Queens gave birth to a male child. On this occasion the amber ball was brought to the King, signifying the event. For a female child another charm of lesser value was utilised.'

An identical ball to the one described above is in a private collection in Britain.

Some amber from Burma travelled north to the Naga people, in what today is Assam. Here the beads tended to be long and cylindrical, with short and long beads strung alternately into chunky necklaces. Unfortunately this market was avidly exploited, along with that of Tibet and neighbouring lands, and many necklaces purporting to come from this area are in fact 'burmite coloured' phenolic resin, i.e. plastic.

China

Ambers from Burma and the Baltic have been worked in China from very early times.

The Chinese treatment of amber has been largely inspired by its different tones and composition, rather than as a single distinct 'amber style'. Thus carvings executed in yellow Baltic amber tend to have similarities to soapstone carvings while the clear, cherry-red burmite is treated in the same manner as translucent jade – often with near-impossible feats of dexterity bearing in mind the brittle nature of clear ambers.

The heftiest Chinese works in amber are the Mountain Carvings. The largest in the world is said to be in the Kunstindustrie Museum of Copenhagen, while a close runner must be that of the Norton Gallery, West Palm Beach, Florida. It will be interesting to see, as China becomes more open, what has also been preserved intact at its place of origin.

These mountains are usually presentation pieces from the emperor to leading literati. In turn, they often depict allegorical presentations. For example, the Florida mountain (dated to the reign of K'ang Hsi, 1731–1795) depicts on one side Wang Po being presented with his younger brother Wang Shao, and on the reverse the presentation of Chang Chung (God of Literature) with his father Wu-Ki. The figures are gathered under trees, and the rock is also decorated with pagodas. This rock measures 27.3 cm × 38.7 cm × 19.1 cm.

Amber carvings

Many carvings of the seventeenth and eighteenth centuries survive, but mostly in museum collections. Occasionally a fine private collection comes on to the market – for example the sale of 1216 amber items from the Kitson collection in the early 1960s (Sotheby, London) – and when such an event takes place, collectors from all over the world gather for the opportunity to learn and reappraise. The catalogue of the Kitson collection (which covered far more than amber among its treasures) is so detailed in the description of the lots, that it is worth reproducing a small part:

'*Tuesday*   *October* 18*th*, 1960
The Property of the late T. B. Kitson, Esq.
(*Sold by Order of the Executors*)
RARE AMBER CARVINGS

49 An amber Shrine Carving of Kuan Yin, Goddess of Mercy, seated in a cave, her hands folded in her deep sleeves, a veil over her head, at her feet a dragon, a tree to one side, $2\frac{7}{8}$ in., the back with an inscription which translates "The Goddess of Mercy, The Universal Door Chapter, if one meets with demons, poisonous dragons and evil spirits, then one should repeat (the Sutra) regarding the power of the Goddess of Mercy and they all dare not to harm one", *Ch'ien Lung*, wood stand

50 An amber Libation Cup, the exterior carved on a minute scale with animals, birds and fish including elephants, deer, a fox, bears, walrus and penguins, the exterior of rich orange colour, the interior yellow, 6*in*., *perhaps Ming Dynasty*

51 A root amber Carving showing three sages under a pine tree and below them a listening attendant, the reverse with three birds perched amongst rock-work and branches, the amber of rich reddish colour, $7\frac{1}{2}$*in. high, on carved wood stand* $10\frac{3}{4}$*in*., *Ch'ien Lung*

52 An amber Carving of Shou Lao, The God of Longevity, a youthful attendant beside him both standing holding a peach, Shou Lao with a bat on his right shoulder and a staff surmounted by a gourd flask in his left hand, his deep-sleeved robes engraved with leafy sprays and *shou* medallions, the amber of warm reddish colour, $5\frac{1}{2}$*in., Ch'ien Lung*, wood stand

53 A pair of amber Carvings of a sage and vendor, the former standing pulling his beard, the latter carying his wares, both with their hair in a pigtail and in flowing robes with tasselled belts, $4\frac{1}{4}$*in.* and $4\frac{3}{4}$*in., Ch'ien Lung*

54 A set of eight amber Carvings of the Pa Hsien, each Immortal standing holding his or her attribute and well carved in amber of warm dark orange tones, $5\frac{3}{4}$*in. to* 7*in., Ch'ien Lung*, the high wood stands carved and pierced with *ling chih* fungus

The group catalogued above, easily identified by their distinctive appearance and emblems has been recognised since the Yuan Dynasty

55 An amusing amber Carving of a warrior mounting a stag, the warrior shown smiling, a flower in his hair, in deep-sleeved robes and with his sword slung behind him, the stag with head turned to one side, the reverse with a hawk in predatory attitude and with two swallows in flight, the whole surrounded by a pierced pine tree, the tone varying from yellow to orange, 6*in*., 17*th Century*, wood stand

56 AN ATTRACTIVE AND EARLY BRUSHWASHER in the form of a lotus leaf superbly carved on the exterior with a flower and stems and with four lizards, the interior with a single lizard and with the leaf tracery delicately engraved, the amber of warm even tone, 4½in., Sung/Yüan Dynasty

57 AN AMBER CARVING OF THE TS'IH-SIEN (Seven Immortals of the Brahmans) shown seated amongst rock-work in a bamboo grove and one standing with a raised cup, the amber of rich dark tone, 6¼in., Ch'ien Lung, wood stand

58 AN AMBER GROUP OF THE TRIAD, each man standing holding his emblem, above them is carved and pierced a cloud scroll formation with the wu fu, the amber of rich orange tones, 8in., Ch'ien Lung, wood stand

59 AN INTERESTING LARGE AMBER BOULDER CARVING of light colour, carved with hunting scenes amongst pine trees and bamboo, showing mounted warriors, archers and others on foot with kylins, tigers, and deer at bay, 8in., Ch'ien Lung, wood stand

60 A FINE AND LARGE IMPERIAL AMBER PEACH BOWL CARVING, the hollow bowl with five-clawed dragon encircling a flaming pearl on a wave scroll background, the whole surrounded by a mass of foliage carved and pierced in high relief with four monkeys and two bats amongst branches of fruiting peaches and lychees, the amber of comparatively dark colour in parts almost clear, a skilful piece of workmanship of the highest quality, 10¼in. long, 4½in. high, seal marks, wood stand.' (Sotheby's Catalogue, 18 October 1960)

Indeed, the catalogue of the Kitson collection is *so* detailed that it was worth trying to trace its history, and eventually an earlier version, manually typed in a loose-leaf folder, came to light at Sothebys. This folder appears to solve several queries which arise from the catalogue – for example: what is the Singapore amber frequently alluded to, or the Indian root amber, or the Persian amber? The latter holds the clue. At the back of the folder is a section where Kitson (for it is now believed that the collector himself wrote these entries) registered the date he had purchased all the items, from whom they were purchased and the purchase price. One particular source, from which many pieces had been purchased, is still known today to advertise Persian amber, etc. as meaning the place where this type of amber was most favoured, manufactured or purchased in its present form, rather than the stricter term for the origin and type of resin. It is very sad that the original owners of that particular shop, the peer group to Mr Kitson, also died in the 1960s, for perhaps with them we lost information about sources of amber and its working, not recorded elsewhere.

Small ornaments from the eighteenth and nineteenth centuries

It can be no coincidence that all over the world connoisseurs of amber eventually focus on small Chinese carvings as the most sought-after items around which to build their collections (*Figure 8.4*). Those most readily available date from the eighteenth and nineteenth centuries and fall conveniently into several categories, described in the following.

Cloudy baltic amber

Pendants and small free-standing ornaments made out of cloudy or osseous amber appear to have been carved in great detail during the eighteenth century, but this declines as the centuries progress until those executed at the turn of the present century are almost free-form, or show very little carving. The Buddha's hand, a fruit or a flower bud were especially popular subjects during the nineteenth century.

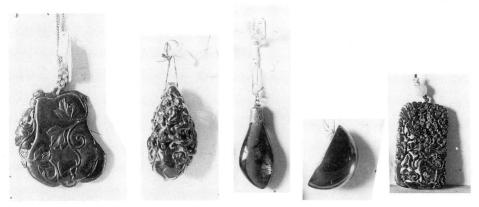

Figure 8.4 Examples of Chinese pendants from the nineteenth century.

The earlier, more detailed carvings are now of a rich orange colour (but this on its own should not be seen as definitive proof of age), and where chipped these retain the original lemon-yellow within. Although the workmanship is often superb, because many pendants especially were carved from quite thin slices, many are broken and have been repaired rather haphazardly in the past (*Figure 8.5*).

Figure 8.5 'Oriental' necklace (nineteenth century).

It has always been a moot point whether large lumps of amber should be cut up into slices or left intact, and commercial reasoning directs the eventual outcome. For example, Williamson records in 1934:

'Messrs. Liberty have in their possession two very large lumps of Burmite from their own property in Burmah, the two being considerably larger than a man's head. From these lumps have been taken slices, sent to China to be carved.'

Clear golden amber

To date, work has not been carried out on a scale large enough to determine the origins of all the clear golden amber carvings made in China. According to Sotheby's sales catalogue of the Kitson collection: 'Large quantities of the amber imported into China is mined in Vladivostok and brought in via the Behring Sea. It is also found in Siam, Cochin-China, Manchuria, Japan, Siberia and Saghalien'.

To this must be added all the amber, natural and clarified, from the Baltic and all the sherry-coloured amber from Burma. While it has been possible from the mid-1960s to separate ambers containing succinic acid from others by means of the infra-red spectrophotometer, and thus the Baltic ambers from the rest, it would need a specific study to undertake this work on a proper scientific basis.

Pointers as to style, however, do exist. Nineteenth century pendants and small carvings tend to be incised but not reinforced visually with dark ink, unlike those objects made of cloudy amber. The only colour markings they do have are simple black dots of pigment for the eyes where figures are depicted. Like the cloudy amber, many pendants from China of the turn of the century are free-form with no carving at all.

Brown burmite and Burmese root amber

Brown ambers have been especially popular in China throughout the period in question, unlike other parts of the world where for long periods brown amber had no value.

Brown ambers have usually been worked into rather solid objects like snuff bottles, large round beads or stocky pendants. They are nearly always all carved in the round, not from thin tablets as is the cloudy Baltic amber. Root amber carvings often have a whimsical construction, the two tones being used to the fullest potential when it comes to design.

Cherry-red amber

Natural red amber has always been held in high esteem in China. Items made out of red amber tend, therefore, to be of a high quality but their numbers are greatly swelled by huge quantities of counterfeit pieces – dyed amber (especially prevalent among Edwardian jewellery), and plastics (long, clear red, faceted necklaces from the 1930s or round, black-cherry necklaces of more recent date).

Genuine cherry-red amber has usually been carved *à jour* into small, flat pendants. These pendants defy description as to workmanship, the recurring motif being fruit among intertwined branches. The zenith of the carver's exhibition of skill is retained for these pieces, the production of which involves hours of patient labour, abrading splintery red resin to expose the branches in the round, without fracturing the slivers that remain part of the design. It is only sad that in the intervening years so many of these *à jour* monuments to patience and skill have been broken. Amber is really much too brittle a substance, especially clear amber, for this type of work, but to view such a piece is quite literally awe-inspiring.

Snuff bottles

Some objects are found in all types of amber and snuff bottles are a good example.

The snuff bottle, worked with a tiny blade set at an angle in a piece of bamboo, was an excellent showcase for amber as the colours of the material are so striking. The bottles are usually of the eighteenth or nineteenth century, and have ivory spoons with hardstone stoppers.

Root amber was perhaps the most favoured variety, the coffee-and-cream colours being so unusual, but snuff bottles are found in all varieties and with all variants of workmanship, from the plain bottle with simple mask ring 'handles', to the grossly ornate bottle with carvings amassed on all surfaces. Plain bottles sometimes have interior paintings. As with all other specialist areas the gemmologist, having identified the bottle as amber, is wisest then to pass the item on to an orientalist for more in-depth identification, should this be sought.

'*Tuesday*   *February 21st*, 1961

The Property of the late T. B. Kitson, Esq.
(*Sold by Order of the Executors*)

RARE AMBER CARVINGS

224 NINE CHINESE AMBER SNUFFBOTTLES with hardstone stoppers, comprising two carved with figure subjects, another with a bat, another plain, another with dragon fish, another with birds in branches, one with cranes, and lotus, one with leaves and insects and one with a kylin, variously carved in opaque and clear amber, the nine bottles in a red leather fitted and lined case
225 ANOTHER BOX OF CHINESE AMBER SNUFFBOTTLES, mainly Chinese and Burmese root amber, comprising: – one elaborately carved in relief with kylins playing; two with parrots, one with lotus medallions, two plain but for mask handles, another with bamboo, one with insects and a Russian Snuffbox in white root amber of flattish shape, all in fitted and lined red leather case
226 NINE CARVED AMBER SNUFFBOTTLES with various stoppers, comprising: – two carved with boys playing with Ichneumon; another with *shua wa wa*; one with rice grain pattern, one with an exotic bird and a pomegranate, another with jumping squirrel and vine, another with a courtier and a maid with pails on a yoke; another with figures in the Taoist paradise and the last carved with a dragon and tiger in root amber, six of the snuffbottles in clear light brown amber, the other three of darker tones, all in a red leather fitted case
227 TWELVE FINELY CARVED AMBER SNUFFBOTTLES with hardstone stoppers, all but two of clear light brown colour, comprising: – one with a fish dragon, the second in root amber and with three goats and monkeys, another with a phoenix and rams, another with figure subjects, another with an equestrienne figure, another in opaque amber with a kylin, a bat, a deer and a monkey, another with a squirrel and insects, another with *t'ao t'ieh* masks, another with a traveller and *wu fu*, one with the phoenix and the dragon, another with Ho Hsien Ku and the last with a dragon and kylin and with crane, pine and deer emblematic of long life, all in a fitted and lined red leather case.' (*Sotheby's Catalogue*, 21 February 1961)

Necklaces

The Chinese mandarin necklace traditionally has 108 beads (*Figure 8.6*) and by Western standards is very large in comparison to Muslim or Catholic rosaries. The complete assemblage consists of the necklace, in three sections usually separated by a jade or quartz bead of greater size, and three pendant sections (*Figure 8.7*). A suspiciously large number of these necklaces have a provenance of the Summer Palace, Peking.

Most Chinese necklaces are of non-graduated, syrup-coloured clear amber, and of

Figure 8.6 Portrait of a Chinese Mandarin showing how the oriental necklace was worn. *Christies, New York.*

Figure 8.7 Rosary of amber and corrundum beads with plaques and pendants of jadeite. *Victoria and Albert Museum, London.*

a simple round design. As with other Chinese ambers of this tone, it is not usually possible to decide whether the resin is from the Baltic or is more local (infra-red spectroscopy not being readily available to the gemmologist), but most Baltic necklaces worked in the Baltic are faceted or of lozenge design, so confusion is minimal. It is also worth noting that Chinese necklaces, unless they are of recent date, i.e. since the late 1970s, are crazed on the surface. As stated elsewhere, crazing cannot be taken alone as evidence of age, but the Chinese use of amber for ornamental purposes stops abruptly in 1912 and does not recommence until the last few years.

There are many carved items of jewellery or objets d'art which are loosely termed Chinese, and although some undoubtedly were made in China, many appear to have been worked by Chinese people in Singapore, or by Koreans, Japanese, etc. Knowledge of Oriental ambers is really at a very early stage of research in the West, and it is to be hoped that funds will be available before too long to alter this situation.

Bibliography

ANDERSON, J., *Mandalay to Mornich* (1876); in: Denny Papers, Mineralogy Library, British Museum (Natural History), London

CHIBBER, H. L., *Mineral Resources of Burma*, Macmillan, London (1934)

DENNY PAPERS, Mineralogy Library, British Museum (Natural History), London

DU HALDE, *A Description of The Empire of China*, London (1738)

GRIFFITH, W., *Journals of Travels in Assam, Burma and Bootan*, Vol 1, Calcutta (1847)

HANNAY, CAPT., 'Route from Ava to the frontier of Assam', *Journal of the Asiatic Society of Bengal*, No. 6 (1837)

LAUFER, B., *Historical Jottings on Amber in Asia*, American Anthropological Association, New York (1907)

NOETLING, F., 'On the occurrence of Burmite, a new fossil resin from Upper Burma,' *Records of the Geological Survey of India*, **XXVI** (1892)

PENZER, N. M., *The Mineral Resources of Burma*, London (1922)

REISS, L., 'Geschichte der Insel Formosa', *Mitteilungen der Deutschen Ges. für Natur- und Volkerkunde Ostasiens*, **VI** (no date; cited by Laufer above)

SEMEDO, A., *History of that Great and Renowned Monarchy of China*, London (1655)

STUART, M., *Records of the Geological Survey of India*, **LIV** (1923)

WILLIAMSON, G., *The Book of Amber*, Ernest Benn, London (1932)

YULE, H., *A Narrative of the Mission sent by the Governor-General of India to The Court of Ava in 1988*, London (1858)

Chapter 9

Amber from Sicily

Natural occurrence

Sicilian amber is known as simetite, from the River Simeto, the main amber-bearing waterway of the Island. Apparently not widely known until the sixteenth or seventeenth century and extremely rare today, it had a brief reign as the fluorescing amber *par excellence*, and was said at its peak to have a value 'approaching that of diamonds' (Farrington, 1903).

The amber is of uncertain tertiary date, possibly Miocene, according to Schlüter (1978).

Its collectability comes from its unusual range of colours, its frequent fluorescence, and its rarity in this century.

It occurs in brownish-grey porous sandstone mixed with lignite, either as scattered surface deposits or later agglomerations. Little is found *in situ*, the majority being collected as well-rounded nodules from the recently dry fiumari, or fast-running mountain rivers, in the springtime after the 75 cm annual rainfall has torn and gouged the soil from the hinterland and brought it down on to the plain (*Figure 9.1*). According to local collectors, in past years when the amber was more plentiful, after particularly advantageous weather, all the amber gatherers used to stand in a row alone the shoreline (*Figure 9.2*), and nobody would start gleaning until the signal was given. How sad that those days have passed.

Sicilian amber has rarely been found in any large size. Buffum (1897) talks of it as occurring in sizes as large as an orange, and Siviero (1954) states that it rarely reaches 8 or 10 cm. This is important as many carvings attributed to simetite are in fact of succinite or Baltic amber, and any large simetite carving should be viewed with scepticism even before an infra-red spectroscopic test is undertaken.

With the exception of Mount Peloritani in the extreme north-east of the island, which is of gneiss and crystalline schists, practically the whole of Sicily is formed of Mesozoic and later deposits. The amber appears to originate in the mountains west of the active volcano, Etna, and has been subject, geologically recently, to both

Figure 9.1 Sicilian Fiumari. The amber is transported by flash floods in the spring.

Figure 9.2 Simeto River mouth showing sand-bar, which restricts distribution of Sicilian amber.

eruptions and earthquakes which have exposed new strata, on a regular basis, to the spring floods. The amber, while containing only minute amounts of succinic acid, does contain a large amount of sulphur; this, and the tectonic disturbances are thought to contribute to its strong fluorescence in natural light.

Ferrara (1805) and Bombicci (1873) probably give the most extensive list of the localities within Sicily where amber has been found. Apart from the mouth of the Simeto or Giarretta south of Catania – always the most prolific areas – the mouth of the Salso at Licata on the southern coast was said to be another source. Ferrara also mentioned Asaro, Centorbi, Leonforte and S. Filippo d'Agiro, Girgenti, Terranuova, Scicli and Ragusa. To these, from other authors, must be added Caltanisetta, Calacibetta and Castrogiovanni. What little amber there is today comes from Nicosia (verbal communication, Fecarrota, 1985). Amber has therefore been found, albeit with paucity, throughout the eastern half of the island, and no single vein in the central mountains has so far been isolated which could be the origin of the material. Thus we have the final resting place of the resin, but not the source.

The fact that simetite appears to be missing from both use and literature in classic cultures is unexplained. Perhaps the particular terrain which contains the resin was not exposed during this period. It is certainly strange that there are so few examples of amber from Syracuse, when one remembers that this was the largest Hellenic city, with 500 000 inhabitants, and that many Greek and Roman myths and legends, often depicted as subject matter on Italic ambers, are actually set in Sicily: for example, the Rape of Prosperine.

It is interesting to plot the brief occurrence of Simetite in literature. Agricola mentions Sicilian amber in the sixteenth century, and Carrera gives quite a lengthy description in his *Memorie Storiche di Catania* (1639):

'The third notable characteristic of particular value which I must mention is the amber which appears on the sea coast of Catania of such an enormous size that it is similar to an orange.
    Many however, are found which are very small in which a small animal is enclosed, such as an ant, a midge, a fly or a flea.
    Since here in our seas of Catania is found a large quantity of amber although it is far distant from any trees but produced by the fire of Etna from bituminous parts of rocks moulded together, we can conclude with considerable justification that this amber is produced from the moisture of the rocks of the sea. I should like to add that there are other parts of the sea in Sicily where this is formed by the characteristics of the cliffs.'

Patrick Byrdone, in *A Tour through Sicily and Malta* (1790), recalls: 'It throws up near its mouth (the Giarretta or Simeto) great quantities of fine amber; this is carefully gathered by the peasants in the neighbourhood and brought to Catania ... They have likewise here a kind of artificial amber, made I am told from copal, but it is very different from the natural.' A century later, in the 1890s, Buffum records: 'the amber found at the mouth of the Giarretta at the present day is limited to a few nodules only'. Although today the collections once made appear to be scattered, at least we have a record of their former wealth. Dr Orazio Silvestri exhibited 600 pieces of Sicilian amber in Turin in 1884 and Buffum, despite his pessimism, was able to purchase at least 150 superb examples during his sojourn on the island.

Denny spent part of 1923 in Sicily and notes that:

'a string of fluorescent amber, every bead a different hue, is a most attractive ornament. Old necklaces, heirlooms of many generations, of this description are occasionally seen worn at fiestas. A curious piece I saw resembled lapis lazuli ... exceptional pieces of this description fetch a very high price – and even small pieces of fluorescent amber of good colour fetch anything from 100 lire upwards.' (Denny Papers)

With the disappearance of amber in the late nineteenth century, the gap was filled by tinted or heated amber (commonly known as Chinese cherry-red amber) so commonly encountered in Edwardian jewellery (*Figure 9.3*) and of course the clear red amber plastic beads of the 1920s and 1930s.

'Especial skill is lavished upon the preparation of spurious Sicilian amber. The yield of such amber is negligible, the Sicilian amber of the ships being Baltic amber artificially coloured.' (Baker, 1931)

Today we have a new threat, for although the author saw some undoubted Sicilian

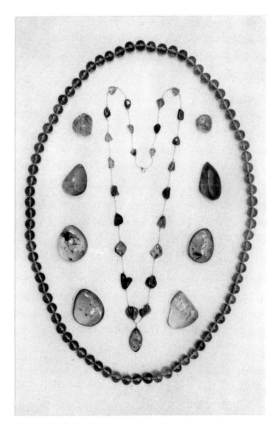

Figure 9.3 Sales display produced by Liberty & Co.,
Regent Street, London in the 1930s: 'Amber charms
from 10/6 to 63/-, Sicilian amber chain 8½ Gns, Red
amber chain 25 Gns'.

amber for sale in Catania during the period 1984/1985, amber in other towns like
Taormina was of more dubious parentage. Schlee and Glöckner (1978) record that
they had been advised by Beiner of the Dominican Republic that much of the local
red resin was being exported to Sicily. There could certainly be confusion between the
yellow ambers, with a natural blue fluorescence, that are found in both the
Dominican Republic and Sicily.

The colour of Sicilian amber specimens in most nineteenth century collections is
now a bright, clear cherry-red, or a gradation between clear golden to orange-red, and
the fluorescent colours have vanished. The apparent loss of fluorescence still needs to
be the subject of considerable research before this phenomenon is fully understood.

Thus the specimens that Buffum wrote about as 'showing sapphire blue, pale rose,
violet, and brilliant ruby' are today merely 'straw yellow and faint olive green', which
he recorded as their 'actual', i.e. non-fluorescing, colour. With age, these have become
redder as will all ambers, and although magnificent, perhaps it is a good thing that he
never realized the transient nature of his gems. The necklace as depicted in the
frontispiece of his book, *The Tears of the Heliades*, and the necklaces left by him to

the Boston Museum of Fine Arts, are probably of identical origin but colourwise they bear no relationship to each other today (*Plate 5c*).

Williamson (1932) wrote: 'On some specimens there are beads or clots, almost resembling rubies in their gorgeous blood colour.' The author has also seen this, but in Dominican amber, and Hunga (1979) talks of Sicilian green amber. However, the work on these 'green' ambers is, in the author's opinion, crude appearing to have more affinity to Baltic workmanship then Italian flair.

Usage

Amber was in occasional use, before the arrival of the Greeks, by the Sikeli people who had taken possession of the eastern half of the island prior to 1500 BC. The Greeks considered the Sicans and Sikeli to be barbarians but their pottery, glass and ornamentation was quite advanced, and may have been influenced by Egyptians, Africans and Phoenicians who all had contact with Sicily at this early date.

In the museum at Syracuse there are rude circular amulets from necropoli at Pantalica and Melilli, and Paolo Orsi in 1890 also records amber beads found by him at the Sikelian necropoli of Plemmirio, near Syracuse and at Castelluccio, near Noto. It would be interesting to subject these finds to infra-red spectroscopy.

It has been conjectured that Sicilian amber was known to the classic cultures but it was called *lyncurion*. Demonstratus said that this was the urine of the lynx, and that the male formed a substance that was 'red and fire-like' while the female, being inferior, formed a paler variety. Philemon called red amber *sualiternicum*, and said that it came from a different region than the more common ambers. However, very little amber, once analysed, from this period is other than Baltic. One must not be confused by the fact that all ambers oxidize to a red colour. It is the colour of the kernel of the amber that is the original colour of the piece, not the surface patina.

Various books were printed in the seventeenth century which contained information about Sicilian amber, and even Agricola, in his great work *De Fossilibus*, records: 'for they dig it up also in Siciliy; where by the violent force of running waters it is discovered, and carried as far as to the sea, and beaten back by the waves of the sea, it is often found upon the shore'.

There is then a gap in our information until the late eighteenth century when Brydone continues:

'... is carefully gathered by the peasants in the neighbourhood and brought to Catania, where it is manufactured into crosses, beads, saints, etc. and is sold at high prices to the superstitious people on the continent. We bought several of these figures and found them electrical in a high degree; powerfully attracting feathers, straws and other light bodies ... some pieces of this amber contain flies and other insects curiously preserved in this substance, and we were not a little entertained with the ingenuity of one of the artists, who had left a large blue-bottle fly with its wings expanded, exactly over the head of a saint, to represent, he told us, lo spirito santo descending upon him.'

Although Brydone says, 'large fine pieces are constantly found at the mouth of the Simetus', this must all be taken with some caution, for it is thought that amber from the Baltic was imported from a very early date to augment the local supplies, especially as it occurred in larger pieces, and cloudy amber is more stable to work than clear amber. The clear-amber religious reliefs in the Buffum collection, and others like them, have still to be put to the infra-red spectroscopic test, and not until then will this matter be settled.

In fact, Sicilian carvings carried out in simetite are one of the great mystery areas still to be explored. Most examples that have survived are in private collections and little of importance is on view in public museums.

In 1787, Sestini published his *Descrizione del Museo d'Antiquaria e del Cabinetto d'Istoria naturale del Signore Principe di Biscari*, which includes a catalogue of the Sicilian amber. Prince Ignazio Biscari (1719–1786) excavated most of the ruins of Catania and his collections were exhibited in the museum which bore his name. Goethe visited his widow and in a letter dated 3 May 1787 describes the palace where he was shown, among other things, a case containing 'urns, cups and other objects of amber, of all shades from deep yellow to the most beautiful hyachinthian red ... for executing which large pieces of a marvellous size must have been necessary'.

Denny writes, in February 1923:

'I endeavoured to find the Palazzo Biscari, eventually succeeded, and arrived at an immense doorway in a street at the back of the Duomo. After ringing the bell for what seemed an eternity, one of the gates was eventually opened. Inside was the usual courtyard with the crumbling remains of what must have been a very fine mansion. The door-keeper was not enlightening. No, the Palazzo was shut up. No, there was no one there, which we well believed as the whole place looked most desolate.'

The author also visited the 'Museo Biscari' in 1984 but found it to be private apartments. The Biscari 'collection' had supposedly been moved to the Museo Civico, but upon inspection all that remain are a single figure of a knight on horseback killing a lion (clear, red amber), a simple stemless pot (clear, red amber), an amber shell of the cockle type and a disc of copal in a metal frame.

Hunga (1979) recounts visits to their London shop, Sac Frères, by a gentleman from Taormina: Mr Leader Williams. This man ran a business from the Palazzo Atenasio where, according to Denny's notes: 'anything of value was taken at night to be sold'. Among the most important things that Denny left among her notes were four fading photographs, with accompanying sales information and price, from Mr Williams' shop. One is reproduced (*Figures 9.4* and *9.5*); the quality is very poor, but they are rare examples of this type of local carving. Although said to be of seventeenth-century workmanship, they are more likely to be of later date. The use of a metal 'tray' around various ambers to form them into a group, appears to be typical of ambers from this source (verbal communication, Fecarotta, 1985).

The ornaments that can, with a fair degree of certainty, be ascribed to simetite without further analysis are the large, clear, double cabochons, made popular by Castellani's revival of antique jewellery of the Etruscan period.

In 1865 Mr J. J. Jeans, British Vice-Consul at Catania, showed at the Dublin International Exhibition, 'an amber necklace of 21 large flattened beads, and 22 smaller ones, of considerable mineralogical interest, the amber being found on the banks of the Simeto ... and being of such various colours, bright red, wine red, reddish-yellow and of bluish tones' (Simmonds, 1879).

Figure 9.4 Group of figures and farmhouse. *W. Leader Williams, Palazzo Atenasio, Taormina.*

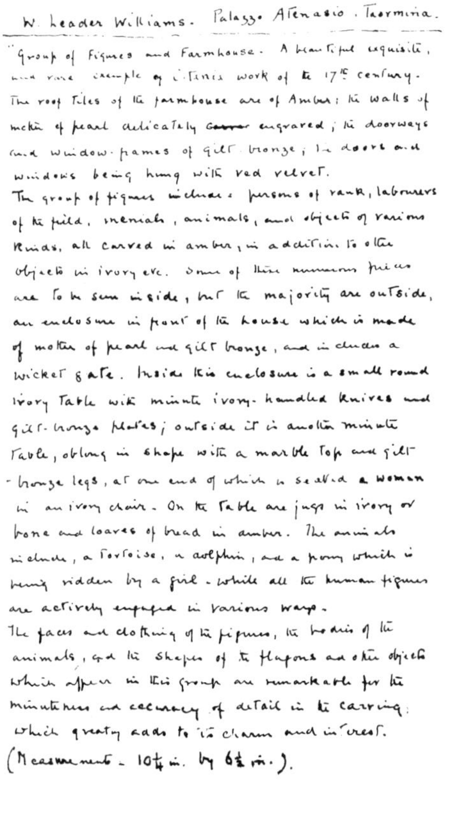

W. Leader Williams. Palazzo Atenasio. Taormina.

"Group of Figures and Farmhouse. A beautiful exquisite, and rare example of intense work of the 17th century. The roof tiles of the farmhouse are of Amber; the walls of mother of pearl delicately ~~carve~~ engraved; the doorways and window-frames of gilt bronze; the doors and windows being hung with red velvet.

The group of figures includes persons of rank, labourers of the field, menials, animals, and objects of various kinds, all carved in amber, in addition to other objects in ivory etc. Some of these numerous pieces are to be seen inside, but the majority are outside, an enclosure in front of the house which is made of mother of pearl and gilt bronze, and in cludes a wicket gate. Inside this enclosure is a small round ivory Table with minute ivory-handled knives and gilt-bronze plates; outside it is another minute Table, oblong in shape with a marble top and gilt-bronze legs, at one end of which is seated a woman in an ivory chair. On the Table are jugs in ivory or bone and loaves of bread in amber. The animals includes, a tortoise, a dolphin, and a pony which is being ridden by a girl - while all the human figures are actively engaged in various ways.

The faces and clothing of the figures, the bodies of the animals, and the shapes of the flagons and other objects which appear in this group are remarkable for the minuteness and accuracy of detail in the carving; which greatly adds to its charm and interest.

(Measurements - 10¾ in. by 6¼ in.)."

Figure 9.5 Rosalind Denny's notes on the group shown in *Figure 9.4.*

Buffum (1897) apparently stumbled on such a necklace completely by surprise when he hitched a lift in Sicily and the girl driving the horse and trap was wearing such an ornament: 'Whilst she spoke, the gems in her necklace flashed in the sunlight, showing colour-shades ranging from faint blue to deepest azure, and from pale rose to intense pigeon-blood ruby red.' Before he left the island he states that he 'succeeded in collecting numerous specimens' (although by this period of the 1890s such amber had become scarce). These were left to the Boston Museum of Fine Arts in 1901 but have sadly still to be placed on permanent exhibition for the public. The simetite cabochons were made into a huge suite of jewellery for Buffum, comprising about 40 ambers, and another 50 were incorporated into a casket measuring 44 cm × 30.8 cm × 46 cm made by Professor Fritz von Muller, Director of the Academy of Arts, Munich. The ambers were cut in 'Italy' in imitation of antique cameos and intaglios. The remaining 72 cabochons were originally made into a display, although today they are kept in a soft leather pouch. See Plate 5.

The same type of jewellery is described by Hunga, talking about a necklace of Sicilian amber given to her mother by Mr Williams: 'The necklace consisted of 16 pendants hanging from a thick gold chain, graduated in size and separated from each other by a linked design of delicate gold pieces. Each pendant was a different colour.'

It is interesting that in 1874 a piece of exceptional beauty was found at Campaola in Italy. This piece of amber was fluorescent, and as large as a fist. It was found near a sulphur mine in the valley of the Senio, in Miocene sand.

Bibliography

BAKER, I., 'Old amber', *Connoisseur Magazine*, December (1931)

BOMBICCI, L., *Corso di Mineralogic*, Bologna (1873)

BUFFUM, A., *The Tears of the Heliades, or Amber as a Gem*, Sampson Low, Marston & Company, Limited, London (1897)

DENNY PAPERS, Mineralogy Library, British Museum (Natural History), London

FARRINGTON, O. C., *Gems and Gem Minerals*, Chicago (1903)

FERRARA, *Sopra l'Ambra Siciliana*, Palermo (1805)

HUNGA, R., *The Magic of Amber*, NAG Press, London (1979)

SCHLEE, D. and GLÖCKNER, W., 'Bernstein', *Stutt-garter Beiträge zur Naturkunde*, C, No. 8 Staatliches Museum für Naturkunde (1978)

SCHLÜTER, T., 'Zur Systematik und Paläkologie harzkonservierter Arthropoda einer Taphozönose aus dem Cenomanium von NW-Frankreich', *Berliner Geowissenschaftliche Abhandlungen*, A, No. 9 (1978)

SIMMONDS, *Commercial Products of the Sea*, AP 463, Ch. 6 (1879)

SIVIERO, R., *Gli Ori e le Ambre del Museo Nazionale di Napoli*, Library of Victoria and Albert Museum, London (1954)

WILLIAMSON, G., *The Books of Amber*, Ernest Benn, London (1932)

Chapter 10

Amber from Romania

As with other deposits elsewhere in the world, there are several ambers of differing geological ages found in Romania. Indeed, to be more exact these deposits range the length of the Carpathian Mountains, and are flushed out eastwards towards the plains.

Ambers have been found and studied over the past 160 years from the basins of the Prut and Dniester rivers in the USSR, following the Carpathian Mountains through Suceava, Piatra Neamt, Bacau, Putna River, Rimnicu Sarat, through Buzau County, the Ploiesti and Ocnita oil deposits, to Craiova and Valzea. Not surprisingly, amber is found intermittently in the province of Dobrogea where the Danube and its tributaries drain into the Black Sea (*Figure 10.1*). In the interior of the Carpathians, yellow amber is found at Sibiu and Alba; in both these cases, the amber is found within large valleys.

The ambers vary in age from Cretaceous to Eocene, and occur in a wide variety of colours. Indeed Murgoci, in his papers of 1903 and 1924, differentiated 160 different tones. These same papers also offer the key to confusion surrounding the term *rumanite*. In 1891, Otto Helm published an article which referred, among other varieties of Romanian amber, to rumanite, a variety of Buzau amber with a brown or reddish coloration. In the century which has since passed, this term rumanite has come to be used for all amber from Romania. In fact, only a small proportion of ambers from this country are found in the range of brown or red; the majority are clear, pale yellow, and far more remarkable for their extensive internal crazing due to geological pressure, than for their unusual hues.

It is possible that the fallacy that Romanian amber is usually black, brown, ruby-red, or even grey, stems from the fact, only just beginning to be understood, that amber which 'imbibes' other substances – gases, minerals in liquid solution, etc. – occurs near the surface in deposits or high on raised land. It is thought by Romanian geologists that Helm did not have access to the more usual tones in sufficient quantity, as the mining of amber at depth was not undertaken in the nineteenth century.

Amber washed out in the spring melt, or found as surface deposits in Buzau

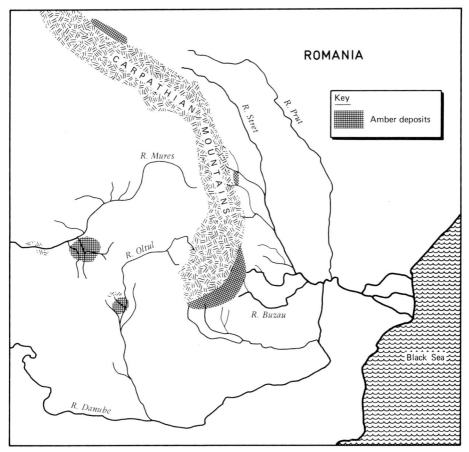

Figure 10.1 Areas of Romania where amber is found.

County, may be any colour within the black/brown/red/greenish spectrum, as well as the common yellow. It is not known at what depth the amber becomes unaffected by the impurities which lead to the more exotic tones.

Murgoci himself mentions that deposits at Le Lac are ruby-red at the summit of the nearby hill but transparent yellow at its base.

The theory that ambers with coloration other than the usual yellow to brown (e.g. the rainbow schiller found on some Romanian amber, or the brilliant blue fluorescence found on some Dominican amber) are found near the surface and not at depth, still needs scientific study. However, the author, and those miners she has talked to, believe this to be the case.

When one considers the localities where amber is found, it is not surprising that some of the resin should be stained brown. In Romania it is frequently associated with oil or tar deposits, and it is known that the resin found while boring for oil and gas in the North Sea is stained brown and black. This latter source, especially from the area around Dogger Bank, has yet to be investigated from the gemmological viewpoint.

Geology

Within the boundaries of Romania, the amber from the Buzau area has received the most attention. Here, as elsewhere at the junction between the Carpathian foothills and the plains, the land is much folded and eroded. Alternating strata of Kliwa sandstone and bituminous or menilithic schist are exposed, often at 60° to the hillside. According to Murgoci, 'the geological horizons correspond exactly to the amber layers (blue earth) of the Baltic Sea'. These rocks are relatively soft and the action of water has released much from the hinterland over the centuries, to be collected by local peasants as curiosities or ornaments.

By contrast, further north at Piatra Neamt the sandstone has been turned by pressure into quartzite and thus the deposit is much harder to work.

In both the Buzau area and Piatra Neamt the amber is found in the 'blue' schist, along with traces of coal and organic deposits. Often a nest of resin is found, usually a large nodule surrounded by smaller pieces of resin. The local people call these 'hen and chicken' deposits. It would seem that they are the result of secondary deposition.

As the Carpathians swing south-west, a third area where amber occurs is in the province of Oltenia. Whereas the ambers from Buzau and Piatra Neamt are Oligocene in date, the Oltenia ambers are found in Eocene strata.

Early workers on Romanian ambers suggested that they should be categorized as follows:

rumanite (from Buzau);
almashite (from Piatra);
muntenite (from Oltenia).

Colour and internal structure

Buzau area

Colours:	Clear yellow, blackish, brown, red due to alteration and 'burnt' (over-oxidized, friable amber).
Internal structure:	Extensive internal crazing due to pressure. Some internal faces reflecting and refracting light and imbibed substances allowing colour-play. Some fluorescence.

Mists of dark inclusions. Insect or plant inclusions rarely identifiable except after close study.

Where internal cracking has occurred in parallel or undulating lines, a mother of pearl effect is achieved. (This latter was always the most sought-after variety commercially, much of it being used for smoking requisites in Turkey and Persia.)

Piatra area

Similar to Buzau amber, but this resin has been subjected to even more geological pressure. Indeed, surrounding rocks are very metamorphosed. The amber is more fluorescent, harder, and when worked smells of bitumen and sulphur. The 'burnt' amber of this area is chocolate-brown rather than black. Fluorescence can be blue, green or purple (as with other fluorescent ambers). Occasionally found with internal structure of 'metallic scales'.

Oltenia province

This amber is clear wine-yellow. It is friable to handle and not found in sizes above 10 cm × 3 cm. Very fluorescent.

Cretaceous amber from Sibiu

Little is known at present about ambers such as that from Sibiu in the internal faction of the Carpathian Mountains. No analysis has been carried out but the associated deposit of fossil plants is of tropical origin (verbal communication, Dr Ticleanu).

Extensive laboratory tests have not yet been carried out on these ambers. The original chemical analysis carried out by Murgoci is reproduced in *Table 10.1*. An infra-red spectrograph of Romanian amber collected at the Colti mine during a field trip in 1984 is reproduced in Appendix 3.

TABLE 10.1. Chemical analysis (%) of Romanian amber (from Murgoci, 1924)

	Carbon	*Hydrogen*	*Oxygen*	*Sulphur*	*Ashes*
Baltic amber	78.63	10.48	10.47	0.42	—
Buzau amber – yellow	79.92	10.19	8.19	1.21	0.49
Buzau amber – blackish (rumanite)	83.29	10.77	4.45	0.93	0.56
Buzau amber – burnt (rumanite)	81.64	9.65	7.56	1.15	—
Piatra amber – blackish (almashite)	79.45	10.23	3.00	1.40	5.52
Piatra amber – clear green (almashite)	82.15	10.94	2.57	0.33	3.51
Oltenia amber – yellow(?) (muntenite)	85.42	11.46	2.55	0.54	0.03

Romanian amber has been used by the local people from antiquity. The earliest piece found in connection with man dates from the Palaeolithic and was found in a cave at Cioclovina. Amber has also been found in a Bronze Age necropolis at Buzau where seven or more amber beads were placed with bronze biconical beads, bronze wire spirals and a bronze bracelet.

From the Iron Age (1200–600 BC), over 5000 amber beads have been found in the same area. A later necklace (200 BC) from Cetateni, Arges district is made up of a large central amber bead, four cowrie shells, a cockle shell and large glass beads. This necklace was found, like the others, on the margin between the Carpathian foot hills and the plain. Two beads from a Dacian tomb were analysed by infra-red spectro-graphy in 1981 by Carmen Coltos in Romania. One was found to be local to the Buzau district and one was from the Baltic. It must be remembered that Romania has long been famous for its natural deposits of gold and salt, so the area has a long history of trading, and even subjugation, by foreign powers keen to maintain direct access to these minerals.

Romanian amber rose to international importance in the nineteenth century, with the fashion for smoking requisites made of fossil resins. Amber was thought not to pass on germs, thus being the ideal substance for pipe mouthpieces, cigarette or cigar holders, and Eastern pipes (*Figure 10.2*).

Amber

Amber

Figure 10.2 Romanian amber mouthpiece on Eastern pipe.

Most of the amber was collected by the local people and exported rough, direct to Vienna and Constantinople. The importance of these two cities to Romanian amber is largely due to the fact that the Ottomans and the Austro-Hungarians both ravaged Romania during this period.

'*Monday*   *January 23rd, 1961*
The Property of the late T. B. Kitson, Esq.
(*Sold by Order of the Executors*)
RARE AMBER CARVINGS

107 A Roumanian amber Brooch, formed of an elliptical cabochon cut stone, mounted in silver, 2¼*in.*; an amber Pendant, an ovoid piece of clear brown amber suspended in the middle of a gold and enamelled setting, 1¾*in.*; a Sicilian amber Pendant of ovoid shape, mounted in gold; and a pair of Chinese ear-rings, the coral pendants carved with *shou* characters.

108 A Roumanian amber Brooch, the elliptical piece of roumanite cabochon cut, 2¼*in.*; a roumanite Ring with square bezel and intertwined serpent hoop; a rectangular clear yellow amber Pendant containing insects, on gold chain; and four other pieces of various amber.

_____

125 A Roumanian Carving of a Dragon, its sinuous tail curled backwards over the scaly body, attractive irridescent golden tones with reddish-brown and black reflections, 3*in.*; and another Group in roumanite of three Lizards sprawling across a rock shown smooth and clear on the underside. 2⅝*in.*

126 A well carved Fish, in Roumanian amber or roumanite, of dark reddish colour with characteristic cracking, 4½*in.*; and a Roumanian amber Head of a bearded man of barbaric aspect, his tousled head with a fillet, the roumanite of orange and brown colour, 1¾*in.*

127 A Roumanian amber Figure of a Monkey, seated chewing a banana, its long limbs covered with shaggy hair, deep reddish-brown tones with paler mottling, 3*in.*; and an amber

Bust of Bacchus, the naked god raising a cup in one hand, a wreath of fruiting vine round his head, dark translucent amber, $2\frac{3}{8}in.$

128 An attractive Roumanian amber Carving of a Dragon, advancing with neck arched and intertwined with its tail, the protruding eyes of ferocious aspect, the roumanite in tones of brown and yellow, showing characteristic cracking, $3\frac{1}{2}in.$

129 A ROUMANIAN AMBER GROUP of St. Christopher carrying the infant Christ across the stream, the bearded saint represented half-length, wearing robes and holding a staff in his right hand, Christ, wearing a smock, rides pick-a-back, the roumanite of reddish-brown colour with darker brown mottling, $4\frac{1}{2}in.$' (*Sotheby's Catalogue*, 23 January 1961)

Fashion was greatly aided by the attention given to Romanian amber at the turn of the century by the Royal Family. Romanian amber necklaces, ear-rings and smoking requisites found their way as royal gifts to people of importance all over the world. Today many of these items are in museums but occasionally they appear at auction when old collections come on to the market. The prices fetched depend on those present – an obvious statement but one particularly the case with rare ambers.

Between the wars, the firm of Grigoresco received a concession of 700 hectares in Colti parish and undertook more systematic exploitation, mining in shafts and galleries. Here, and elsewhere, the wooden props (made of freshly felled pine, making the mines aromatic) were used over and over again; thus galleries collapsed when no longer in use. In some areas, despite the rarity of amber, it was found in quantities of 1 kg per metre. Indeed, on occasion up to 3 kg per metre were recorded at Colti Isv. Budarului where one of the earliest collectives was established.

During this period in Bucharest, the Geology Laboratory possessed a lump of 3204 kg, and the Mineral Laboratory one of 2473 kg, but these and many others may no longer exist due to the sustained bombing of the city in the Second World War and the not infrequent earthquakes. In 1984, the building where many specimens were housed was still in the state of reconstruction, and if any specimens did survive their whereabouts are unknown.

A lump weighing 1785 g was found by children after a storm in 1975 in Colti parish where it is now housed in the local museum. Where polished, it is seen to be clear on the outer surface and cloudy or dense in the interior portion. This latter also exhibits the internal crazing or cracking so often associated with Romanian amber.

Locally, in the Colti district, amber has no doubt always been collected even it is has only been exported afar during periods of high demand. In 1578, a legal document was drawn up which mentions many-coloured *chihlimbar* (the local word: from kiah-ruba, Persian for straw-puller). Fata Budei made rudimentary galleries between 1829 and 1934, and in 1902 the engineer Grigorescu began his explorations.

Grigorescu, as mentioned in an earlier paragraph, received a concession of 700 hectares which yielded 67 kg in 1923, 130 kg in 1924 and 120 kg in 1925. However, by 1935 the exploration had ceased. In 1948 all exploration became the right of the government.

The Colti Collective Museum was constructed between 1980 and 1983 and gives a very fine backdrop to the Romanian amber displayed within. Much of the enthusiasm for the project has come from the influence of Mr Christian, who lives locally and has for many years worked amber into necklaces and lucky talismans. Christian works this local amber with a motor-driven grinding wheel, and polishes with powdered gypsum.

Most of the amber is washed out during the spring melt into the local river system and, as one would expect from surface deposits, its colour ranges through rich dark brown, black, and sparkling mottled yellow.

Today, the amber of Romania is not for sale commercially. It is found in such small amounts, even with state-run mining, that it is at the moment retained for scientific and curiosity value rather than for trading purposes. This situation may alter, as more and more amber is collected and stored at a central point, as has been happening for at least the last ten years.

In one area, a pioneer mine is now producing clear yellow amber at the rate of the measure of one Kilner jar a week (weight not known). This amber is extensively fractured internally; indeed, the break in the resin is not conchoidal but that of irregular intersecting prisms. It was thought that this was accentuated by the method of extraction – a pneumatic drill was being used to prise open the rock – but geologists inform me that the pressure on the amber running in veins at 60° deep into the hillside would already have created this internal fracturing.

The mine has a gallery extending 100 m into the hillside and a shaft upwards has been constructed into a higher vein. This second gallery is now being worked above the first. The amber-bearing stratum is said to be the widest in the area but even so it is only about 3.5 m in height and width.

If it can be proved that the more exotic colours of amber occur near the surface, it may be more financially rewarding in the long term to undertake a series of shallow mining ventures, paying particular attention to the strata removed by the water system when it is in flood. The stratum at Colti is extensively faulted, so the amber-bearing seams come to the surface in many places within a small area.

If the surface deposits were systematically evacuated, the more usual methods of water and even salt solution could be employed – there is an abundance of both in the area. Romania at present is undergoing great financial constraints and any process that involves the use of natural products should be considered seriously alongside the perhaps more natural recourse to high technology.

Amber tends to occur in water-absorbing schist/leutite, and is often removed *in situ* with its matrix. This matrix can usually be softened over a period if steeped in water, and the lumps can either be 'felt and removed by hand', as in the Dominican Republic, or floated away once in a saturated brine solution, as in nineteenth-century Prussia.

These methods are slow and tedious, but when one considers that at the turn of the century the mother-of-pearl coloured amber (*sidef*) was valued at 3000 francs/kg and that to make a cigarette holder it frequently took several blocks joined together to gain enough length, such careful exploitation may be financially viable. At the same period, the red/metallic/fluorescent ambers were fetching 800 francs/kg. It would be exhilarating to see again *sidef* and garnet-red Romanian amber on the gemmologists' shelves, but the tampering or dyeing of the more frequent clear yellow amber will have to be watched. It has not been done to date but the temptation – perhaps many miles away from source – will be great.

Characteristics

Refractive index:	1.4377
Specific gravity:	1.03–1.12
Hardness:	2.5–3.0
Melting point:	330–350°C
Colour:	Usually transparent. Pure yellow through reds due to ageing to 'burnt amber'. Brown, black or grey due to impurities. Never boney
Special features:	Extensive internal fractures which may reflect light or be stained darker colours by impurities
Lapidary factors:	Hard and takes good polish. May give off fumes of bitumen, sulphur or hydrogen sulphide

Bibliography

COLECTIA MUZEALA COLTI, Souvenir brochure (1983)

MURGOCI, G., *Gisements du Succin de Roumanie*, l'Imprimerie de l'État, Bucharest (1903)

MURGOCI, G., *Les Ambres Roumains*, Correspondance Economique de Roumanie; Bulletin officiel du Ministère de l'Industrie et du Commerce, VI-e année, No. 6 (1924)

WILLIAMSON, G. C., *The Book of Amber*, Ernest Benn, London (1932)

Chapter 11

Amber from the Dominican Republic

There has been some confusion in the gem world following the appearance of large quantities of amber from the Dominican Republic. Initial reaction has been guarded – that it is not amber at all, or that there is something, unspecified, wrong with it. In fact, this amber was first noted by Christopher Columbus in the fifteenth century during his second voyage to the West Indies, and by the early twentieth century its appearance was being widely reported in quite obscure journals. The following is taken from the *Transactions of the Dumfriesshire and Galloway Natural History and Antiquarian Society* (Labour, 1914–1915):

> 'A few years ago an interesting discovery of amber was made in the island of San Domingo. It appears to exist in considerable amount, and often in pieces of good size suitable for making carved objects of much beauty. It possesses a fluorescence similar to that seen in some of the amber from Catania, Sicily.'

The lack of identity for Dominican amber is explained by commerce, for until 1979 Germany purchased nearly all the amber direct from the island, and back in Europe it was mingled with Baltic amber, its source unacknowledged. Today, any piece of amber has to be polished by the Dominicans before exportation and it is against the law to export rough resin.

The Dominican Republic comprises the eastern two-thirds of the island of Hispaniola. It covers an area of 48 442 km^2 and is traversed by two mountain ranges: the northern Cordillera Septentrional and the Cordillera Central, which boasts the highest peak (Pico Duarte) in the Caribbean (*Figure 11.1*). The climate is subtropical (30–55°C), and the Spanish-speaking population of five million is concentrated in three or four large towns, leaving much of the hinterland unpopulated and unmapped.

The amber found on the island is of several varieties, thought to be of differing

The substance of this chapter first appeared as an article by the author in *Journal of Gemmology*, **XVIII,** No. 4 (1982).

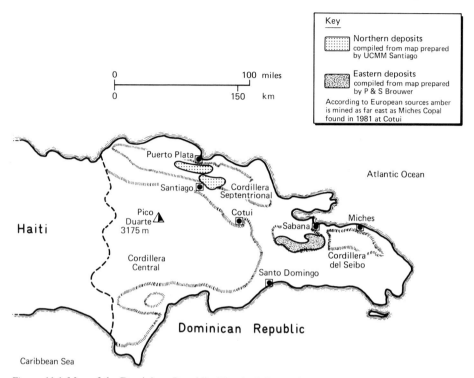

Figure 11.1 Map of the Dominican Republic. The shaded areas indicate amber deposits.

geological ages, though in the main from the Oligo-Miocene period; however, resin found in 1981 at Cotui is much more recent and should be classed with copal. The finding of a variety of ambers in one place is a common phenomenon; the amber from the Baltic region varies in age from Jurassic (bornholm), through early Eocene (Danish mo-clay deposit, which does not contain succinic acid), to late eocene (Samland Peninsula). Due to a deterioration in the climate, the formation of amber in the Baltic seems to have stopped early in the Oligocene, somewhat later in Romania, while it was still functioning in the Miocene in Sicily (Larsson, 1975, 1978).

Jean Langenheim, of the University of California (1969), gives a list of geological occurrences and botanical affinities between some 50 ambers, using infra-red spectroscopy to match absorption peaks in fossil and modern resins.

Comparisons of infra-red absorption spectra featuring Dominican amber appear in papers by Langenheim and Beck (1968) and Saunders *et al.* (1984). Six spectra of Dominican amber are shown in the former paper: four came from the Santiago area and gave a similar trace, but two from Palo Quemado gave more generalized spectra – possibly due to increased oxidation.

Following the author's visit to the island in 1981, the Natural History Museum in London made a series of infra-red spectra tests on the samples (see page 125).

For the purpose of this report, the two major amber deposits are referred to by the geological formations in which they occur. This is to prevent the oft-repeated errors which arise due to duplication of place names on the island.

Amber from the Altamira formation

Amber is found scattered in a 60 km^2 area to the north and east of Santiago de los Cabelleros, in the Cibao valley. Within this area lie the deposits of Los Cacaos, Palo Quemado and Loma el Peñón, which produce high-quality amber. The amber-bearing strata are exposed along three faults within the cordillera Septentrional in the northern part of the island included in the Bahamas Arc. This fact is important, as it has long been speculated that there might be rich amber deposits in Haiti, which occupies the western third of the island, but the arc does not extend into Haiti.

The amber occurs in a sequence of limestone, sandstone, mudstone and conglomerate, exposed by tectonic movements. It is restricted to the grey carbonaceous mudstone beds and is often associated with lignite. The mines of La Toca are associated with the upper NW-SE fault, those of Los Higos, Pulido and Rio Arriba with the central fault, and those of Palo Quemado and Los Cacaos with the lower SE–NE fault. The strata around the mines are extensively faulted, and altitudes vary from 300 to 1000 metres within short distances.

Table 11.1 gives a concise description of deposits, from a local university project undertaken in 1979 (Diaz *et al.*).

TABLE 11.1. Amber deposits in the Dominican Republic (from Diaz *et al.*, 1979)

Location	Altitude (m)	Observation
Palo Quemado	420	Along a fault-line, on the eastern side of Palo Quemado stream
West of Pulido	720	Near a fault-line, in unconsolidated mudstones
Near La Cumbre road	700	In layers of carbonaceous mudstones
Rio Amina	460	On the west bank of the Arriba River, in a well-cemented sandstone
Los Cacaos	620	Unconsolidated clay
Loma de Carlos Diaz, Rio Licey Blanco	500	In a massive material (limolita arenosa)
La Toca	700–800	In layers of Carbonaceous mudstones

The steeply sided hills are covered with rough pasture in tropical hardwood forest, and access between settlement and mine is usually by footpath only. This difficult terrain hinders large and modern extraction of the amber, and most of the mines are simply holes, dug to a depth of 3–6 metres with the aid of pickaxes and shovels. There are many accidents due to landslips and seepage of water into the workings.

Two mines were visited in the area. The first was about a kilometre off the La Cumbre road, down one side of a steep hill, across the boulder-strewn river in the valley and about 100 metres up the other side. A vein of grey mudstone was being extracted from the sandstone hill, the miners working at some distance from each other to prevent landslips. The holes were dug with pickaxes, the harder sandstone being retained as a roof support. The mudstone was then collected in large tin cans or sacks and passed to workers outside the mine, who washed the loosely consolidated mudstone with water and removed the amber. The extraction of the amber was unsystematic, and it was not clear why the mudstone was not taken to the nearby river to be washed in running water. One of the mines had caved in three weeks before, and the owner was laboriously clearing away the overburden with the help of a wheelbarrow (*Figure 11.2*).

Figure 11.2 The mine owner at La Cumbre clearing the debris from a cave-in.

The second mine was about 10 km distant and we were able to take the university Land Rover to the site. Here a group of 20 miners were stripping the top-soil with the aid of a bulldozer (*Figure 11.3*). The machine had been hired by a merchant in Santo Domingo, the capital, and he was to take a percentage of all amber found. The

Figure 11.3 A group of miners.

expense would be justified, in the miners' view, as the amber they hoped to locate was of the blue fluorescent variety which commands the highest prices for export. At both mines I was told that the blue amber outcropped at the top of the hills, near the surface.

Amber from the Yanigua formation

There is a certain lack of agreement between Dominicans and Europeans about the characteristics of amber from the east of the island. I have found it to be a much brighter yellow, and brittle under the diamond-saw, unlike its northern neighbour which can be sliced very finely indeed and is most satisfactory to work with.

The following information about amber from the Yanigua area is taken from a treatise prepared by Brouwer and Brouwer (1980). It represents the Dominican viewpoint.

The amber from the east of the island is softer, and is thought to be younger than that of the north. However, its large size and the predominance of blue and green fluorescing varieties has encouraged the extraction of amber from this remote and inhospitable site since the 1950s.

The Yanigua sedimentary formation is of Miocene age and its amber has much in common with amber found in Chiapas, Mexico. Amber-bearing strata occur in a series of small valleys, bounded to the north and west by the Los Haitos karst platform, and to the south and east by igneous rocks, in part belonging to the Cordillera del Seibo. The sediments are similar to those of the Altamira: limestone, clay and carbonaceous mudstone (Lutite). The amount of lignite associated with amber declines westwards. The sediments are horizontal with little tectonic movement except at La Cumbre (El Valle zone) where the formation has tilted.

About 15 small mines are concentrated around Sierra de Agua, Colinia San Rafael and Yanigua, the outcrops at Sierra de Agua being at the top of the formation and Yanigua the base. Extraction is by pickaxe, the mudstone is softer than in the northern formation, and up to 36 kg of amber may be found in a pocket. Problems associated with a difficult terrain (altitude varies from 100 to 400 m) and a high rainfall (2000 mm) limit mechanization, although transverse trenches are dug at Sierra de Agua and intermediate platforms for collecting waste are frequently constructed.

The amber is usually very clear and clean, and the fact that it is of larger size than that of the Altamira is possibly due to the area having experienced less tectonic disturbance. Inclusions in the amber from this location have been analysed at the Smithsonian Institution in Washington and were found to have associations with *Hymenaea*. This is the tree thought to have produced the amber from Chiapas, Mexico and is of especial interest as it is an extant species, now growing near mangrove swamps in the tropics (*Figure 11.4*).

The largest piece of amber found on the island to date comes from the Yanigua, although it is invariably credited to the Altamira in translated literature available overseas. It weighs 8 kg and was found in March 1979 in Sabana de la Mar County. The piece is now displayed in Santo Domingo in the Plaza Criolla. Another fine piece, weighing 4.8 kg, was displayed in the summer of 1982 at an exhibition of amber in

Figure 11.4 Hymenaea courbaril. Royal Botanic Gardens, Kew.

Schaffhausen, Switzerland. The provenance of this piece is not known apart from the rough designation of 'northern Cordillera'. It was found quite recently by a child planting a coffee bush. Both these pieces are oval and flat, and are of a dense, rich brown colour similar to burmite.

Colour

The majority of amber from the Dominican Republic is of a transparent, golden yellow colour. This is often not realized, for much of the amber appears to be a rich mottled brown but this colour is due to detritus included within the clear yellow amber. Very little of this 'brown' amber reaches Europe, most of it being exported to the USA where it commands high prices for curiosity value. The yellow grades from almost colourless (which I found for sale only at Puerta Plata on the northern coast) to a deep red. This latter is often due to a portion of the rough exterior being retained to lend depth of hue, a point confirmed by the frequency of crazing still being present, associated only with newly polished amber of this colour. Dominican amber will redden due to oxidation, in common with other ambers. Several sacks of rough amber were examined at source in the mountains, and three or four pieces of ruby-red, deeply crazed amber, which had a 'rusty' coating similiar to Italic amber carvings, were extracted. I had previously been shown lignite by the miners and told that this was 'over-ripe amber'; they were not convinced of the truth when shown the friable deep red amber.

The blue fluorescent amber is an interesting phenomenon as the brilliant oily sheen appears by reflected light as a surface effect. The blue can in some cases be replaced by green or even purple hue, and these pieces are much sought-after.

The finding of fluorescent amber (rather than amber placed under ultraviolet light in a laboratory) is very exciting, as it was previously thought that this type of amber came largely from Sicily (simetite). The Sicilian finds are now rare and, as the colour appears to fade once the amber is taken from the ground, the likelihood of ever handling any has diminished. Pompelio Brouwer had some Dominican 'blue' amber photographed for an American magazine in 1977, and when it is examined today, only a few years later, the marked deadening of the colour is very apparent.

Schlee (1980) has undertaken a detailed study of this natural fluorescence and considers it to be due to the spread of organic particles emanating from wood, induced during a heating and melting of the amber lump (possibly due to volcanic action). Certainly the blue is evidenced widely in deep brown, multi-inclusioned pieces. Amber which is quite clear and yet still shows a blue or green tinge is rare; it is very possible, however, that these pieces were altered by their close proximity to the more common wood-included amber.

Cloudy amber is rare. I only have one piece in my possession: a deep orange with cream swirling clouds. This is quite unlike anything else and bears a close visual affinity to amber found in Arkansas, USA.

During my visit, I also purchased three cloudy pieces of green amber: one blue-green and two olive-green. Green amber is very rare indeed; I only saw one other piece, placed in a jeweller's window in Santo Domingo. It measured 5.1 cm × 2.5 cm and had been carved into a frog.

Inclusions

The Dominican amber is rich in inclusions. Over 100 species have been identified already and, because there is no mechanization, most of the insect, plant or mineral 'fossils' are seen by the labourers before they are lost in the production of amber jewellery.

Cataloguing of inclusions is now being carried out in Germany, Switzerland and the USA with a number of relatively large inclusions giving much excitement.

Occasionally the inclusion will have retained its colour. There is a famous example of a beetle with brilliant green iridescent wings, and flies with red or yellow eyes. The inclusions which I find most interesting are those which depict movement: ants carrying young grubs, or fighting termites. Dr Paul Whalley, of the Natural History Museum, London was kind enough to examine a series of inclusions brought back to this country, as follows:

Specimens 1 and 2:	Contain small parasitic wasps (Hymenoptera)
Specimen 3:	A large peltid beetle, a scolytid beetle and a fly
Specimen 4:	A caterpillar – probably an early instar of a noctuid moth
Specimen 5:	Fragments of plants, a beetle and a delicate gall-midge
Specimen 6:	A spider and termites – the latter are the family Termitidae and are workers.
Specimen 7:	Plant debris
Specimen 8:	Plant debris
Specimen 9:	Crane-fly (Diptera, Tipuldae)

Specimen 10:   Parasitic wasps (Hymenoptera)
Specimen 11:   Mordelid beetle (Coleoptera)
Specimen 12:   Lepidoptera, gelechoid moth

One of the termites and the caterpillar skin are being investigated more fully, and the plants are to be dealt with at a later date.

Little work has been carried out to date on the mineral inclusions, and unfortunately the paper by Flamini, Graziani and Grubessi (1975) did not cover Dominican amber. However, I have observed two-phase (gas-bubble in liquid) inclusions, and metallic dendritic forms. I found no sun-spangle stress inclusions in Dominican amber, confirming the findings of Crowningshield (1977–1978).

Infra-red spectra

G. C. Jones, of the Department of Mineralogy, British Museum (Natural History), obtained the infra-red spectra of five of the Dominican specimens using a Perkin Elmer Model 683 spectrophotometer (*see* Appendix 3). A few milligrams of each resin were ground with dried potassium bromide and pressed into discs before recording their spectra over the wave number range 4000 to 400 cm.

(1) 'Best Santiago Amber.' A pale yellow-brown, cohesive resin, difficult to grind.
(2) La Cumbre (Santiago deposit). A deep red resin.
(3) and (4) 'True Green Amber.' Two pale green, cloudy carved specimens bought in Santiago or Santo Domingo.

These four specimens gave similar spectra, typical of retinite-type fossil resins. The differences in the spectra are almost entirely in the intensities of the two peaks at 1640 and 885 cm^{-1} and hence are probably related to age or degree of oxidation.

(5) Miches specimen. This clear yellow, easily friable material gave a typical copal or recent resin spectrum with sharp intense peaks. The spectrum closely matches those of some African copals in the collection of the British Museum (Natural History), particularly those from Sierra Leone, Congo and Zanzibar.

The Miches specimen has the highest volume content and shows the strongest 1640 and 885 cm^{-1} peaks, while the others show a progressive decrease in the intensity of these peaks together with a general broadening of the spectral pattern from specimens 1 to 4. These other spectra also show a gradation between the two Dominican types given by Langenheim and Beck (1968) and have a close resemblance to their type 1 spectral pattern for amber from Chiapas, Mexico.

Manufacture

Most of the amber is transported from the hills by mule, and polished in the larger towns behind the merchants' shops. Even the smallest pieces are used, the outer crust being removed on an emery or wooden wheel, and the finish applied with tripoli powder and a cloth wheel. The poorer pieces are sold by street vendors and, although cheap, are usually chipped and ill-matched when examined in detail. The only evidence I found of processed amber was the production of tiny chips into cast resin picture-frames. From the gemmologist's point of view, the most dangerous development has been the coating of recent copal-like resin, which comes from the Cotui area, with an epoxy compound to render it more stable and less likely to craze. This venture, to my mind, has put in doubt the whole production capacity of several hundredweight of genuine fossil resin a year and, unless it is stopped or the government press for it to be sold under a separate name, I foresee major problems.

Amber has been finished into jewellery on the island since the 1950s, when a Cooperative of the Industrial Artists was set up by the government. The best jewellery is made under direction from Germany or the USA, but the Dominicans seem happier to produce at their own pace, without western-imposed regimes of order-dates and completion schedules.

The quality of the native jewellery is poor. This is very sad, as the quality of the amber is excellent. What seems to be missing is a sense of pride or self-discipline, which would ensure that the beads of a necklace were at least drilled through the centre or that pendants were finished without cavities due to slipshod workmanship. I found only one merchant on the island who stocked really first-class items, but unfortunately he was not on the government list of official exporters and I have had monumental difficulty in obtaining shipments from this man.

The design of the jewellery is pleasing; the clear, limpid character of the resin lends itself to the production of free-form pendants and pastille-drop necklaces. Bands of soft wire are bound around the amber lumps to make them secure, and attached to each other by S-linked chains. This style of jewellery is very distinctive and is unique to Dominican amber.

Much of the carving is geared to the American market. Americans have long visited the island in cruise ships, and larger lumps tend to be carved with North American Indian braves. Smaller lumps depict Central American folk art or even Buddhas. I asked about this strange subject matter and was told that the market tended to divide into the ethnic and the antique, so that Dominicans covered both spheres. Less common were carvings of elephants, domestic animals, or odd mis-shapes glued together to represent mushrooms, a man walking his dog, a couple sitting on a bench, etc. However, the pieces I consider a real success are the heart, leaf or natural drop-shaped pendants; these are quite beautiful and merit a place in any jewel box.

Bibliography

BROUWER, S. B. and BROUWER, P. A., 'Geologia de la Region Ambarifera Oriental de la Republica Dominicana', 9na Conferencia Geologica del Caribe (1980)

CROWNINGSHIELD, R., 'Developments and highlights at GIA's laboratory in New York', *Gems and Gemmology*, **XV** (12), 367–368 (1977–1978)

DIAZ, N. J., DIAZ, H. J. and RODRIGUEZ, J. J., 'Geolo-gia de los Yacimientos de Amber en la Cordillera Septentrional al Noreste de Santiago', Santiago University internal paper (1979)

FLAMINI, A., GRAZIANI, G. and GRUBESSI, O., 'Inorganic inclusions in amber', *Archeometry*, **17**, 110–112 (1975)

FRONDEL, J. W., 'X-ray diffraction study of fossil elemis', *Nature*, **215**, 1360–1361 (1967)

FRONDEL, J. W., 'X-ray diffraction study of some fossil and modern resins', *Science*, **155**, 1411–1413 (1967)

FRONDEL, J. W., 'Fossil elemi species identified by thin-layer chromatography', *Naturwissenschaften*, **56**, Heft 5, 280 (1969)

GIL GIL, N. DE JS., LANZO, G. and PLOSKONKA, E., 'Desarrollo minero del Cibao', Santiago University internal paper (1980)

LABOUR, N., 'Amber and jet in ancient burials', *Transactions of the Dumfriesshire and Galloway Natural History and Antiquarian Society*, **III**, 106–120 (1914–1915)

LANGENHEIM, J. H. and BECK C. W., 'Catalogue of infra-red spectra of fossil resins (ambers)', *Botanical Museum Leaflets, Harvard University*, **22**, 117 (1968)

LANGENHEIM, J. H., 'Amber: a botanical inquiry', *Science*, **163**, 1156–1167 (1969)

LARSSON, S. G., 'Palaeobiology and mode of burial of the insects of the Lower Miocene mo-clay in Denmark', *Bulletin of the Geological Society of Denmark*, **24**, 193–209 (1975)

LARSSON, S. G., *Baltic Amber – A Paleobiological Study*, Entomonograph Vol. I, Scandinavian Science Press, Denmark (1978)

ROTTLANDER, R. C. A., 'On the formation of amber from Pinus resin', *Archaeometry*, **12**, 35–51 (1970)

SANDERSON, M. W. and FARR, T. H., 'Amber with insect and plant inclusions from the Dominican Republic', *Science*, **131**, 1313 (1960)

SAUNDERS, W. B., MAPES, R. H., CARPENTER, F. M. and ELSIK, W. C., 'Fossiliferous amber from the Eocene (Claiborne) of the Gulf Coastal Plain', *Geological Society of America Bulletin*, **85**, June, 975–84 (1984)

SCHLEE, D., *Bernstein-Raritäten – Farben, Strukturen, Fossilien, Handwerk*, Staatliches Museum für Naturkunde, Stuttgart (1980)

SCHLEE, D. and GLÖCKNER, W., 'Bernstein', *Stuttgarter Beiträge zur Naturkunde*, **C**, No. 8 (1978)

ZAHL, P. A., 'Golden window on the past', *National Geographic Magazine*, **152**, September, 423–435 (1977)

Chapter 12

Amber from Mexico

Amber from the Chiapas State of Mexico first came to the notice of the rest of the world at the turn of the century.

'Specimens of a very remarkable amber have occasionally been brought by travellers, for the last 15 or 20 years, from some locality in southern Mexico. The only information gained concerning it is that it is brought to the coast by natives, who say it occurs in the interior so plentifully that it is used by them for making fires. The colour of this amber is a rich golden yellow, and when viewed in different positions, it exhibits a remarkable fluorescence. A specimen in the possession of Martius T. Lynde measures $4 \times 3 \times 2$ inches, is perfectly transparent, and is even more beautiful than the famous so-called opalescent green amber found in Catania, Sicily. This material would be extremely valuable for use in the arts. Amber was formerly used as incense by the Aztecs, and fragments have been found on the altars of ancient temples, also in the Catholic churches in early Mexico.' (Kunz, 1892)

The amber is thought to be of Upper Oligocene to Lower Miocene date, and occurs in a sequence of calcareous sandstones and siltstones, exposed by fault or landslide. The major section of strata is exposed near the old town of San Cristobal de Las Casas, where the amber is found in veins or horizontal beds along the face of a 1000-metre fault and also at the foot of the cliff.

Amber is also found in the alluvium near the Huitapan River, Simojovel District, Chiapas, and at two recently discovered sites near Totolapa, on the banks of the Totolapa River, and in a number of streams and arroyas half a mile to the north of the village.

The amber, thought to come, like many Central and South American resins, from the Leguminus genus *Hymeraea* (*Figure 12.1*), is found in fist-sized pieces, and even at the Totolapa village sites the local people net between 1 and 3 kg of rough amber a week. Inclusions are common and, as the vast majority of the golden amber is clear, they are easier to investigate than in some other ambers.

The amber is polished and sold as talismans or jewellery. Popular designs are those relating to the Aztec and Mayan cultures, crosses and beads. To date, this amber is not known to have been exported and reworked in any quantity. It has been used in

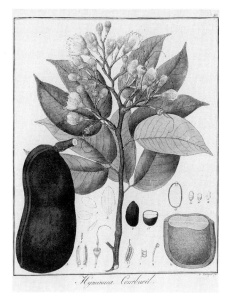

Figure 12.1 Hymenaea courbaril – detail. *Royal Botanic Gardens, Kew.*

past centuries for the production of lip-rings, ear-cylinders and other facial orna-ments, by the people of what today is Mexico and its neighbour Guatemala, and it is usually represented in ethnographical museums.

Bibliography

BRYANT, D. D., 'The "Secret" of Mexican amber', *Gems and Minerals*, November (1982)

JOHNSON, P. W., *A Field Guide to the Gems and Minerals of Mexico*, Mentone, California (1965)

KUNZ, G. F., *Gems and Precious Stones of North America*, p. 302, reprinted from *Popular Science*

Monthly, April 1886; Library of Gemmological Association of Great Britain (1892)

LANGENHEIM J. H. and BECK C. W., 'Catalogue of infra-red spectra of fossil resins (ambers) – North and South America', *Botanical Museum Leaflets, Harvard University*, **22,** 117 (1968)

Chapter 13

Resins confused with amber

There has been confusion since early days between fossil resins and those of more recent date. To the former category belong ambers from the Baltic, Sicily, Burma, Romania and some of those from the Dominican Republic, while the latter covers the resins and gums known as copal, dammar and kauri. The former are millions of years old, while the latter may be formed even today.

The greatest confusion, sometimes wilful deceit, is found where the 'amber' is linked with some ethnographic interest. Many 'ambers' from Africa (*Figure 13.1*), the

Figure 13.1 A Peulh woman from West Africa wearing typical 'amber' jewellery.

Middle East or Asia are suspect – a situation which can lead to all such 'ambers' being dismissed without further analysis, which is a pity. However, the following examples are typical of those which immediately ring alarm bells for the gemmologist:

'Yemen's Jewish community, most of which emigrated in 1948, was renowned for its silver and amber jewellery; you may be lucky to find some but it is expensive.' (Harvey, 1982)

'In India, they use it in many fair works with musk, civet, benzoin, and other sweet things mixed together, where of they make fine apples and pears wrought with silver and gold which they bare (in their hands) to smell upon'. (Bovill, sixteenth century)

Copal

Copal is the name for a large group of resins obtained from living trees and also sometimes found in a fossilized condition. Recent tests at the Research Laboratory of the British Museum in London, using radiocarbon analysis of selected amber and copal specimens, showed surprisingly that no copal tested was over 100 years old (Burleigh and Whalley, 1983).

The word copal possibly stems from the Sanskrit and means 'moon juice'. Copal, in *Shakspear's Hindoostanee Dictionary*, is rendered chandaras – a corruption of the Sanskrit. The Sanskrit compound chandarasa, or moon juice, also appears linked to the resin sandarac.

Among the various kinds of East African copals the best is Zanzibar animé, the hardest form of copal, produced by a species of *Trachylobium*. This part of Africa was formerly German East Africa so the association with copal and amber in trade is a natural one.

Copals are also produced, either historically or currently, from Tanzania, Mozambique and Madagascar in East Africa, along the west coast intermittently from Sierra Leone to Angola, and centrally in Niger and Zaire. The variety of trees producing copals covers *Guibourtia copallifera* in Sierra Leone, *Cyanothyrsus* in Ghana and Niger as well as various species of *Daniellia*, and *Colophospermum mopane* in Zaire and Angola. The trees naturally occurring are according to climate; these trees are not cultivated species planted by man.

Resins from South America are also included in the general term copal, the most famous being *Demerara anime* – Columbian and Brazilian copal. Many of the Central and South American copals show botanical affinities to *Hymenaea*, especially the extant species of *Hymenaea courbaril*.

Historically, by far the most important source of copal was from the island of Zanzibar, now part of Tanzania. Copal was and is found in two distinct conditions: recent, called *chakazi* or *sandarusiza mit* (corrupted by the traders to jackass copal), and ripe or fossil copal.

Lankester, writing in 1900, noted that the raw copal found at the foot of the trees, or tapped from it, did not reach Europe in commerce, but went instead to India and China where it was used for coarse varnish. The ripe or hardened copal was found at a depth of 0.9–1.2 m, not in association with the parent tree. This resin was cleaned of its goose-flesh white skin, and then shipped to Hamburg in Germany and to British ports. Sometimes copal also reached Britain via Bombay, and these shipments may have included the jackass copal.

> 'Copal diggings are conducted by the natives in a careless and desultory manner and the whole trade is surrounded with difficulties. The supply is considered inexhaustible ... The amount annually exported is subject to great fluctuations which equally affect the market value ... It is found in pieces ranging from the size of small pebbles, up to masses of several ounces in weight and occasionally lumps weighing 4 or 5 lbs have been obtained.' (Lankester, 1900)

Copals have occasionally been used instead of true ambers for ornamental purposes: 'The Chinese have learned to imitate amber admirably in a variety of articles made of copal, shellac and colophony' (Wells Williams, 1901). The copal used seems invariably to have been of a clear golden colour, often with insects as inclusions. Three carvings given as examples are a fish and a Buddha's hand finger citron (*Figure 13.2*), both from China, and a European Christian cross. They are all probably of nineteenth-century workmanship although the fish was catalogued as Sung Dynasty (AD 960–1280).

Figure 13.2 Nineteenth-century Chinese carving, in copal, of a finger citron fruit. *Victoria and Albert Museum, London.*

Figure 13.3 Agathis australis – the source of kauri gum. *Royal Botanic Gardens, Kew.*

Carvings, and indeed beads made of copal rather than fossil amber, age differently so they are not too difficult to tell apart. Copal is still volatile and the essential oils will soften when they come into contact with ether. A drop of this substance left on the surface for a minute will partially dissolve the resin, and pressure by a fingertip will leave an impression on the softened area. Copal thus treated, or even vigorously rubbed, will emit a strong aroma whereas any such aromatic perfume from a true fossil resin would be immediately suspect. Contrary to general belief, working amber does not fill the room with pungent smells of pine trees. The smell is distinctive and much more subtle.

The crazing on the surface of copal rather than amber is also different. Copal crazes in tiny, shallow white areas, the undersurface of the resin crumbling off like dandruff when the piece is allowed to dry out. The crazing on amber is not usually two-dimensional, i.e. the cracks go directly into the piece, and do not then turn at 90° causing the surface to flake. The instability of the surface of copal carvings is a real problem when it comes to conservation. The Chinese used to lacquer their best resin carvings and perhaps this is the solution. The most urgent case I have come across was a piece in an American museum. The carving was in the same showcase as some amber snuff bottles, and was suffering considerably from the heat of the illumination. So much so in fact that it was surrounded by a little pile of 'dandruff'; the surface was literally being baked and was cracking like the crust on a loaf of bread.

Old copal necklaces again often exhibit this different form of crazing, leaving the surface dull or dirty-looking. Any syrup-coloured, clear resin with this dried-up surface should be tested with ether immediately. Sadly, many examples of insect or plant inclusions in resin from old Victorian collections turn out to be of recent specimens caught in copal.

Occasionally, copal has been blended with amber chips. This is not very satisfactory as the result is like an ancient version of polybern – the outlines of the harder resin still being visible within the whole. It should also be pointed out that copal will react to fast modern drills and other machinery. It breaks up completely. When drilling copal or recent resins, one can be left with a series of strings of softened matter flying away from the drill like spun sugar threads.

In the 1970s, Tanzanian amber again appeared in the shops masquerading as true fossil amber. It was pale champagne coloured, and worked into simple designs. Any clear, pale resin should be tested as it is frequently of recent date and therefore unstable, and quite unsuitable for ornamental purposes.

Dammar

Dammar is obtained from a variety of different tree species in Malaysia and the Pacific Islands, but principally from *Dammara orientalis*, now renamed *Agathis dammara*. Resins like Manila copal are softer than the African copals and make inferior varnish.

The Department of Minerals and Energy for Papua New Guinea included on the 1979–1982 Development Plan a Dammar Gum Extraction Programme. Two extension officers had been trained in the techniques of resin collection, cleaning and packing, and it was hoped to have a production target of 100 tons a year, providing income for 20 full-time gatherers.

The tree grows, for example, on the high mountain ridges of the Molucca Islands. It can attain a great height and girth but the timber is inferior. The resin is soft, transparent and dries in a few days, when it turns white with a crystalline appearance.

It often flows spontaneously from the tree in such quantity that it hangs in masses like icicles beneath the ruptures. Incisions are made, especially in the knots of the tree, and resin is taken directly from the incisions. It is used in Asia for domestic purposes and, although it is used as a varnish, it has a tendency to turn viscid.

Kauri gum

Kauri gum comes from the tree *Dammara australis* or *Agathis australis* (*Figure 13.3*). This tree is still found on the North Island of New Zealand: its timber is white and close-grained, and of such durability that for many years it was used for the masts of sailing vessels. Other species are found in the Fiji Islands, New Hebrides and Australia. The earliest kauri found on these islands is of Miocene date.

Resinous sap oozed from fractures and ruptures in the bark of the tree. It congealed to form lumps of gum which eventually fell to the ground and were buried by layers of forest debris. The bark often split where branches forked from the trunk and accumulated there also. Strong gales sometimes fractured the heart of a tall tree and it bled internally, with a chalky white gum collecting, often in large amounts, among the giant's roots. Highest quality gum was hard and bright and usually found buried at shallow depth on the hills. Exposure to the sun or even bush fires could transform dull, opaque lumps into higher quality transparent gum. When dug up, the lumps of gum usually had a rusty weathered zone around them and were encrusted with soil. This had to be scraped off and eventually sorted.

In order of decreasing size, the pieces of gum were known as nuggets (sizes B1 and B2), nubs, peas, chips and, finally, dust. Colour could vary from white or pale amber to black. The purest gum had no impurities, whereas the lowest grades of chips and dust had up to 75% foreign material.

Virtually all kauri gum was found in the region where kauri forests grow today, from the lower Waikato and Coromandel Peninsula northwards.

Until about 1850, most gum was collected from the surface, but after that recovery was by digging. In hill country, where soil accumulation is slow, the ancient gum was usually buried at shallow depths, seldom deeper than 1 m. In wetlands and peat swamps it could be buried to depths in excess of 5 m by thick deposits of sediment, etc. In the sand dune county of Aupouri Peninsula, buried gum, together with kauri logs and stumps, occurred in three or four layers up to 4 m or more below the surface. There had been a succession of forests. Each had been killed and buried by advancing sand dunes, on which a further forest later grew. The gum was also found buried in beaches and mudflats, and in great concentrations on narrow peninsulas, and washed out into swampland.

Today farmland, especially vines, orchards and dairy farms are found in this area. In hilly country the decayed, buried head of a kauri tree would yield a bagful of gum.

In the 1880s, the easiest 'bush gum' to recover was from around the base of large kauri trees, where it had accumulated over hundreds of years as the fresh resin dropped from the trunk and branches. Large quantities of gum also accumulated in the forks of the branches, high up in the tops of the trees.

The trees were bled with horizontal V-shaped cuts (known as 'taps'), which were spaced about 40 cm apart around the circumference of the trunk and 2 m apart vertically. Every six months the climber returned to collect the exuded gum and make fresh incisions.

A heated debate arose over the damage gum bleeding was, or was not, doing to these valuable timber trees, but it soon became apparent that the uncontrolled practice was killing many of the kauri giants. Legislation was passed in 1905 that banned bleeding in all state-owned forests; bush gum was a category on its own. The equipment used by the gum diggers was as follows:

(1) Gum spear (pointed steel rod with a spade handle) was used by most gum diggers to locate buried gum. The spear varied in length from about 1 to 8 m.
(2) The hooked spear was for use in swamps, etc.
(3) The spade, a skelton, was specially designed for gum digging, being strongly constructed with a hand-forged steel blade and steel straps, extending half-way up the handle. Sharpened with a file.
(4) Axe.
(5) Bucket.
(6) Carrying sack or pikaus (Maori flax kits).
(7) Small flour bag, used while digging, for temporary storage.
(8) Primitive hand-held pump, made of piping or jam tins soldered together.
(9) Jack knife for scraping surface of gum.

The first people on the fields were the Northland Maoris, later joined by Maoris from the Waikato, King Country and Bay of Plenty. By the 1880s the gum fields were truly multicultural, with many immigrants from England, Russia, Germany, France, Malaya, Finland and Mediterranean countries. The ethnic group to have had the greatest impact on the gum fields were the Dalmatians (and Croatians), who came from the Adriatic coast of Yugoslavia from the 1880s onwards. By 1900 their numbers had reached 5000.

The Maori people called kauri gum *kapia*. Fresh gum was used like chewing gum and passed around on social occasions from member to member in a group. Buried gum was also softened by soaking it in water and mixing it with the milk of the Puwha thistle. Kauri was used to light fires, or bound with flax, ignited and used as a torch by the fishermen at night to attract fish. The Maoris also used kauri for tattooing. The gum was burnt and powdered, and then mixed with oil or animal fat and poured into the tattoo cuts.

The gum diggers, of many nationalities, made ornaments of large kauri lumps by shaping them into the heads of Maori menfolk (*Figure 13.4*). Some survive today and their excellent state of preservation has come from the fact that these ornaments were painted, using oil paints, to show the tattoo marks all over the faces. This coating has protected the gum underneath and prevented it crazing.

Most of the kauri was exported to Britain and America for the production of varnish, and this trade peaked in 1900 when over 10 000 tons were exported. By the 1890s, there were over 20 000 people employed in gum digging but the best gum had been extracted by 1910.

Only a small proportion of the gum was used for the production of beads and mouthpieces for smoking requisites. It was not very suitable for either but this was

Figure 13.4 Head of Maori; shaped from a large kauri lump. This type of work was usually done by immigrant Dalmatian miners.

especially the case with smoking requisites for, unless the older varieties of gum available were used, although the mouthpieces smelt fragrant they were too fragile for heavy use.

By the 1910s spear-found amber was difficult to obtain, but the industry was kept buoyant by the use of kauri being transferred away from varnish and into the production of linoleum. For this purpose the gum required could be of inferior quality, and even chips and dust had a market. The swamps and alluvial flats were worked extensively during this period. Land was drained and the kauri extracted by means of saline floats or vacuum tanks.

The rise in synthetic products killed the market for kauri gum in the twentieth century. Various methods were used for short periods to revive the industry but the gum was nearly worked out anyway, and much of the land was turned over to farmland on government subsidy. In the last two decades very small quantities have been used in violin varnish and in the manufacture of dentures. According to Neil Hanna, of the Gemmological Association of New Zealand, polished jewellery made from kauri gum is still popular with visitors.

Resins

The following is a strange collection of resins which have little in common, but anyone familiar with amber is usually expected also to have a brief knowledge of these ancillary substances used in varnish.

Figure 13.5 An advertisement for an importer of varnish gums which appeared in *Varnish Making*, published for the Oil and Colour Chemists Association, London, in 1939 by Heffer's of Cambridge.

Sandarach

This is a brittle, yellowish, transparent resin imported from North Africa, where it exudes from the bark of the *Tetraclinis articulata*. True sandarach comes from the common juniper and is sometimes also called juniper gum.

The Persian (Iranian) lexicon explains *sandar* or *sandarah* as a yellow gum resembling amber, and the word is also found in *Shakspear's Hindoostanee Dictionary* as *sandarosa* – used in both Arabic and Persian. Arabic writers frequently confused sandarach and amber.

Sandarach is used, on account of its hardness, as an additive to softer resins, and it used to be used as a spirit varnish for photographic negatives, labels, bookbinding and wood preservation.

Lac (shellac)

Gum lac is the product of the *Coccus lacca* insect. These live on the twigs of various trees which they cover with a resinous coating from their bodies, together with eggs and a secreted purple colouring. The eggs hatch inside the gum and more and more gum lac is built up by successive generations. When the twigs are covered to about half an inch the local people pick them and dissolve away the colouring matter in hot water. The purified resin is then packed into coarse bags and melted until it oozes out, and in this state it can truly be called shellac. Its colour range is from clear orange to dark brown, and it is imported traditionally from India, Thailand and what used to be called Indo-China.

Fifty per cent of all shellac used to be purchased by the manufacturers of gramophone records, but today it is simply used as a very superior varnish.

Mastic

Mastic is a resin obtained from the tree *Pistacia lentiscus*, from which it oozes in pale yellow tears. If allowed to fall to the ground it becomes impure, so it is usually collected direct from the tree. Obtained principally from Greece, it is a valuable varnish by itself or may be blended with other resins such as dammar, sandarach or rosin.

Rosin

Rosin is produced from various living species of pine. Found as an oleo-resin, it is separated by distillation into the resin called rosin or colophony and turpentine. Rosin is used extensively on the bows of musical instruments.

Frankincense

This comes from the silver fir or *Abies alba* and is a gum of pinkish colour and agreeable odour. The frankincense of the scriptures was the gum of *Boswellia serrata*, now known as olibanum.

Myrrh

Myrrh is a resin of *Commiphora*, a native of Arabia and Turkey. It exudes from the tree in thick yellow drops, which harden and darken on exposure to a reddish-brown colour. It is brittle and waxy, with an aromatic balsamic smell.

Varnish

The word *varnish* seems to have derived from the Greek *veronice* or *verenice*, which has later been distorted to *vernice* or *bernice*. This latter is interesting as it combines the Greek stem-word and the German word for amber itself – *Bernstein*.

Legend states that in 243 BC Ptolemy Evergetes returned safely from an expedition to Syria, and in gratitude his Queen, Berenice, dedicated a lock of her golden hair in the Temple at Zephyrium in lower Egypt. However, the golden tresses disappeared and it was said that they had been turned into a constellation of stars high in the heavens. Part of this legend has survived into the twentieth century for a group of stars under the name of Coma Berenices is still marked on astrological maps.

The introduction of the distillation of amber for varnish is attributed to Arnaldus de Villa Nova in the thirteenth century, and certainly it appears that it was an early Flemish practice to use Strong or Amber varnish mixed with the colours in paintings to give the paint a flowing texture. The artist Van Eyck wrote a whole treatise on the preparation of varnish, and from the numerous notes, chiefly derived from the Flemish painters which appear in the Mayerne manuscript, there can be no doubt that amber still merited the title of 'vernix Germana' in the seventeenth century.

Amber varnish is hard, slow-drying and dark in tone, and thus has limited application. In Italy it was used on musical instruments – it is especially associated with lutes or stringed instruments from Cremona. In Britain it was recognized as the best varnish for carriages, being so weather-resistant, and it had a brief world-wide application in the early photographic industry.

Beeswax and resin must have been one of the earliest recipes for varnish, but the recipes with regard to true amber varnish fall into three methods. The amber is first dissolved in an oleo-resin like turpentine; or the amber is first fused and then dissolved in oil – this gives a dark and very slow-drying varnish; or the amber is added to boiling oil without fusing – in which case it does not dissolve completely.

There is considerable evidence of the use of the words *amber varnish*, when in reality copal or sandarach have been substituted, firstly because they are cheaper to procure and secondly because they dissolve more easily. True amber varnish is a combination of colophony of amber, oil of turpentine and linseed oil.

Gedanite

From the word *Gedanum*, an ancient name for Gdansk in Poland. It is known to workers as brittle or unripe amber. It is usually transparent, or strongly tranlucent, and of a clear syrup tone. Most of the pieces have the appearance of having been rounded and rubbed, and dusted with a fine white powder. It can be turned on a lathe but not bored, so it is not suitable for beads or similar items; when it has been so used it was usually by mistake.

Several other resins are found with succinite in the Baltic but only gedanite is used for ornamental purposes.

Glessite

From *glessum*, the ancient Aesti word for amber. Usually opaque brown with numerous microscopic cavities and dusty enclosures. It is harder than succinite.

Stantienite

From the nineteenth century manufacturers Stantien and Becker. A deep brown or black resin, with no succinic acid. A resemblance to coke.

Beckerite

As above, but a dull brown, matt colour.

Other natural substances mistaken for amber

Ambergris

Ambergris is a grey, waxy substance obtained from the sperm whale. It has little connection with amber resin, being used as a fixer for perfumes, but must be recorded in a book about amber as it is from the arabic word *Anbar*, for ambergris, that we have through some confusion come to adopt the word amber in the English language. We are not alone for this stem-word is found all over Europe – *ambre* in French, *alambre* in Portuguese, *ambar* in Spanish and *ambra gialla* in Italian. Remembering that the Greeks and Romans did not use this stem-word, it probably spread with the Moors in the early Medieval period.

Ambergris can be considered like a stomach or kidney stone, for it only occurs where the digestive tract has received some infection and been punctured, with the result that acids have eaten away the natural lining. The ambergris appears to be the whale's attempt to overcome this illness.

According to Williamson (1932) the substance often includes tiny black particles from the mouths of octopuses, and it could be these that have scratched and lacerated the surface of the stomach or intestine. One of the earliest references to have survived is from a book of 1398, by Trevisa: 'the whale hap gret plente of sperme . . . and yf it is gaderid and dryep it turnep to be substaunce of ambre'.

There is a jewel in the Metropolitan Museum of Art, New York, which once belonged to the great collector J. Pierpont Morgan. The ambergris is decorated with precious stones and was no doubt worn as a fertility amulet.

Oriental imitations

The Chinese seem to be the most adept at imitating amber with other natural substances. Records exist of dyed sheep's horn, the upper part of the crane's bill and many similar substances, but the most curious must be as follows:

'Amber can be made from chicken eggs: take an egg, mix the yolk and the white of it, and boil it. As long as it is soft, an object can be cut out of it; this must be soaked in bitter wine for several nights, until it hardens; then rice flour is added to it.' (Shên nung pên ts'ao ching – Ko chih ching yüan)

Bibliography

BOVILL, E. W., 'Musk and amber', quoting John Huyghen Van Linschofen (sixteenth century manuscript); in: Denny Papers, Mineralogy Library, British Museum (Natural History), London

BURLEIGH, R. and WHALLEY, P., 'On the relative ages of amber and copal', *Journal of Natural History*, **17**, 919–921 (1983)

HARVEY, N., 'Sanaa – still waiting for the boom', *Middle East Economic Digest*, June (1982)

HAYWARD, B. W., *Kauri Gum and the Gumdiggers: A Pictorial History of the Kauri Gum Industry in New Zealand*, The Lodestar Press, New Zealand (1982)

LANKESTER, SIR RAY, *Diversions* (1900)

TREVISA, British Museum Library (1398)

WELLS WILLIAMS, S., *The Middle Kingdom*, New York (1901)

WILLIAMSON, G., *The Book of Amber*, Ernest Benn, London (1932)

Chapter 14

Gemmological tests for the identification of amber

The tests for the identification of fossil resins, and their separation from plastic or other common substitutes, fall into two categories: the profoundly simple and the extremely complex. The normal range of equipment available to the gemmologist – refractometer, dichroscope, heavy liquids, etc. – has no place in the day-to-day identification of amber. Luckily, however, most of the equipment that is necessary is not expensive.

The saline solution test

Amber has a mean specific gravity of 1.08 and it will therefore float in a salt solution of 10 teaspoons of table salt in 250 ml of water. These quantities can be mutiplied if it is necessary to test large items. Most plastics, and all the pre-war plastics in common use, have specific gravities higher than that of amber so they will sink (*see* Chapter 7). Items should later be washed in water to remove the saline crust which would otherwise develop.

Limitations

Amber items with a badly crazed surface should not be tested in this manner, as the salt water may penetrate behind the cracks and lead to yet further deterioration.

The saline solution test will not differentiate between amber (SG 1.08) and more recent natural resins, collectively termed copal (SG 1.06). The test is obviously not practical where there are metal fixings, and care should be taken to remove air bubbles, especially from hollow items.

Some relevant specific gravities are as follows:

Polystyrene   1.05
Copal   1.06

Amber	1.08
Salt solution	1.12–1.14
Cast phenolic	1.26
Casein	1.33
Glass	2.00–6.00

Heavy organic liquids like bromoform, toluene or methylene iodide must never be used as they will attack both amber and many of its substitutes.

Surface resistance to solvents test

The surface of a piece of copal (kauri, dammar, etc.) will be dissolved when a drop of ethyl alcohol is placed on it for a period of one minute (choose an inconspicuous spot). The surface becomes tacky and an imprint of a finger can often be made where the ethyl alcohol is in contact with the resin. A strong aromatic smell is usually released and, on drying, a white chalky mark may be left behind.

Occasionally – as when the author made tests on the Perowne Collection, Cambridge in 1976 – amber will be affected, but very seldom. In that instance 2.5% of the amber tested did react, even though it was definitely amber and not copal.

Limitations

This test is useful for distinguishing between amber and more recent natural resins. It is somewhat destructive to old carved copals (of which there are a surprising number), and must therefore be carried out with caution on these pieces. Repolishing of the tested portion of the surface will usually be necessary and may spoil the overall patina.

On a basic level, perfumes and hair sprays will damage the surface of amber jewellery over a period of time. The surface will become dull and opaque, and the items will need repolishing.

According to Helm (1891), the eventual solubility of amber is as follows:

Alcoholic solution of potash	40–55%
Oil of terpentine	25%
Carbon disulphide	24%
Ether	18–23%
Alcohol	20–25%
Chloroform	20.6%
Amyl alcohol	20%
Methyl alcohol	13%
Benzol	9.8%
Petroleum ether	2.2%

(no details given as to strength or temperature of potassium hydroxide)

Differential crazing between clear golden ambers and copals

Little seems to have been written about the different ways in which resins appear to craze, or crack, on the surface. Yet it is a fact that all resins do crack, as well as some of the early plastics, and this may warrant further investigation. Old copal, that is copal that has been exposed to the atmosphere for a century or so, will show a surface of tiny interlinked cracks. These cracks run parallel to the surface, and often beneath it. Eventually, minute pieces flake away. This phenomenon is especially evident on older Chinese carvings where the object has been warmed up each day in a brightly lit museum cabinet. Sometimes this 'dandruff' around the item is the first indication to a collector that the piece may not be amber after all. The crazing on copals usually has a *white* overtone.

Amber which has undergone atmospheric weathering for a century or more will also exhibit crazing, but it is subtly different. The crazing on amber seldom leads to the 'dandruff' effect, although the item may become extremely fragile – indeed, to such an extent that sometimes plastics are used to provide stability to the surface. This crazing usually has an overtone which is *darker* than the amber that surrounds it.

The author has noticed that Sicilian and some Dominican ambers craze with a few large intersecting cracks rather than a multiplicity of tiny ones.

Streak and hardness tests

Streak tests should not be carried out on ambers as they are destructive and not very informative. The surface hardness of a piece of amber will vary, not only with variety but also depending on the conditions it has encountered since its extraction from the earth.

What is useful is to run a knife or razor blade across an inconspicuous part of the article. Unless the blade is new and therefore unusually sharp, amber and copal will come away in chips, while plastic imitations can be pared, the surface coming away in curling ribbons. Most fossil resins can be powdered easily. Most synthetics are difficult to powder by grinding.

Tests involving heat

Chips or ribbons of material from an item to be analysed form one of the most useful tests to distinguish not only amber from plastic, but also types of plastic from each other.

Many books recommend the hot-point needle test, where a heated needle is pushed into the surface of the item under analysis. This test is not only potentially destructive, but even dangerous with nitrocellulose plastic. Also, a surprising amount of skill is required to distinguish one plastic from another with such a tiny sample.

To be preferred are tests where small samples are taken from the underside or a concealed surface of the piece (care being taken that the sample obtained is free from lacquer, dirt etc.), and the tiny parings or chips are either exposed to flame or placed inside a test tube and then heated. The latter method is the best as the smell is concentrated. This method is also safer as samples from some plastics 'jump' when heated and could obviously cause an accident. The following should be observed: the smell, melting point, flame type, flammability, stickiness, etc. of the sample. *Note*: succinite, when heated, gives off what many consider to be unpleasant odours. It may have been used as incense in a past age, but for testing purposes one is far too close to enjoy the smell. It is copals that issue the strong aromatic smell so often cited.

In a laboratory, amber, when heated in a glass retort connected to a cooled receiver, will separate by distillation into amber oil and crystalline succinic acid at the neck and colophony at the base of the retort.

Static electricity

The fact that when amber is rubbed it becomes negatively charged and picks up small pieces of paper, etc. is not a test for identification purposes as too many plastics have the same ability (experiment with ball-point pens).

Bibliography

HELM, O., *Schriften der Naturwissenschaftlichen Gesellschaft Danzig*, **vii,** No. 4 (1891)

Chapter 15

Laboratory techniques for the identification of amber

Agricola (1546) appears to have been the first to separate what we now know as succinic acid from baltic amber. Lé Mery (1675) later recognized this substance, then known as flos succini, as an acid. Such early scientific interest in resin may seem surprising but one must remember that during this period amber was widely used in a medicinal context. Later, Heyer (1787) established early reliable physical constants for Baltic amber, and the first thorough chemical study of this resin was published by Berzelius (1827–1828).

Today, many tests carried out on fossil resin are beyond the experience and financial constraints of the gemmologist. These are the tests carried out by such august institutions as the Labour für Bernsteinforschung, Rheinisches Landesmuseum, Bonn, Germany; the Subsurface Geological Laboratory, Saskatchewan Department of Mineral Resources, Regina, Canada; the Amber Research Laboratory, Department of Chemistry, Vassar College, Poughkeepsie, USA; the Mineralogical Society of the USSR, Leningrad; the British Museum (Natural History) and the National Gallery, both in London.

Most of the research is undertaken to obtain more information about the possible plant families that have left behind fossil resins, and the geographic spread of these resins. No one method is the universal panacea, and those described in this chapter serve merely as an introduction to this complex topic.

The following techniques can be used in a laboratory to 'fingerprint' resins by analysis of their constituents. Infra-red spectrometry, thin-layer chromatography, mass spectrometry and differential thermal analysis all measure effects due to the different *molecules* present in the sample. Emission spectrometry and neutron activation analysis are used to detect and quantify the inorganic elements present (as trace elements or impurities). X-ray diffraction measures the characteristic arrangement of *atoms* in crystalline compounds.

146

Infra-red spectrometry (see also Appendix 3)

Substances of any type (gases, liquids or solids) can be identified by their tendency to absorb light energy of infra-red wavelength. The resulting absorption spectrum makes it possible to analyse complex mixtures quantitatively, to identify impurities and to determine the various kinds of atomic groups in the molecule.

The chemical structure of amber is both complex and variable: sufficient to say that it consists of many different molecules, made up mostly of carbon, hydrogen and oxygen in differing but characteristic configurations.

It is possible to pass infra-red radiation through a compressed pellet of approximately 2 mg of powdered amber mixed with potassium bromide (the latter is transparent to infra-red radiation), and to record the frequencies that are absorbed. The fingerprint thus obtained is shown in graph-form by plotting absorption against frequency or wavelength.

'All spectra, both of ambers and modern resins, show more similarities than differences in the region from 2.5 to 8 μm (4000 to 1250 cm^{-1}) where absorption bands are due to stretching and deformational vibrations of functional groups which are little affected by the intermolecular environment.

The upper region of the spectra, 8 to 15 μm (1250 to 625 cm^{-1}), shows greater variety in pattern and differences between resins. As a kind of fingerprint this upper region is useful in grouping fossil resins which not only have similar basic structures, but which sometimes can be related to recent resins. Absorption between 8 and 10 μm (1250 and 1000 cm^{-1}) is due to carbon–oxygen single bonds; it is rarely possible to assign these bands to specific structural features.

Although, in general, the absorption bands above 10 μm (1000 cm^{-1}) are still more difficult to assign, the bending motions of hydrogen atoms attached to unsaturated carbon atoms cause absorptions which yield useful information. In fossil resins the most important of these is the sharp band near 11.3 μm (885 cm^{-1}) which can be attributed to out of plane bending of the two hydrogen atoms of the terminal methylene group. The absence of this band in fossil resin spectra, however, must be interpreted with caution, since terminal methylene groups are easily oxidised.

Amber samples from different ages and locations *generally* give characteristic spectral patterns. A single, relatively consistent pattern *may* characterise an amber from a given locality.*

Although there is some variability, over 500 spectra of succinite from the Baltic Coast give a recognizable, repeatable pattern. In other localities, such as the Alaskan-Arctic Coastal Plain, amber gives *several* characteristic patterns. Some spectral patterns, like those of Baltic succinite and New Zealand ambrite, appear in several geographic areas and different geologic ages.' (Langenheim, 1969)

Beck began analysing resins with an infra-red spectrophotometer in 1964, and by 1982 more than 5000 specimens had been analysed by the Vassar College laboratory (Beck, 1983) It became clear to these researchers that Baltic amber, or more properly succinite, can be distinguished from other European ambers by a nearly horizontal broad shoulder between about 8.00 and 8.5 μm, followed by a more intense absorption at about 8.7 μm. By this means for the first time (setting aside various

*However, this uncertainty makes the assignment of provenance or botanical origin dubious when dealing with a completely unknown sample, except in the case of 'Baltic' succinite (comment from G. Jones, British Museum (Natural History), London).

nineteenth-century methods involving the dry distillation of succinic acid from resins) it was possible to differentiate between items made of say 'Baltic' succinite, and simetite or other non-succinite European ambers.

Beck has been studying the origin of resins found in Mediterranean archaeological contexts with a view mainly to determining trade routes and, although the validity of infra-red spectrometry in such cases is questioned (Rottländer, 1970; Savkevich, 1981), he maintains a high success rate which is difficult to disprove, due to the very large number of spectra made by Vassar in comparison to other laboratories. Savkevich (1981) considers the natural occurrence of succinite in Europe to be too widespread to give clear indications of origin, but does acknowledge that where the natural boundaries are smaller, as for example in Japan, this is a useful method of analysis (Fujinaga, Takenaka and Muroga, 1974).

There are, of course, variations in the appearance of the graph for any given sample. Oxidized amber (which happens to contain a good deal of succinic acid, and leads to yet more confusion in the eyes of the layman) gives a 'smoother' spectrum, with the shoulder assuming a more or less negative slope. Conversely, modern resins, or those with a higher percentage of volatile components, give a 'spiky' spectrum. Naturally, because there are more components in modern as opposed to fossil resin, these graphs also show additional features such as a peak at 6.1 µm.

It must be noted, however, that with regard to non-European ambers botanists (Langenheim, Broughton and others) have found ambers with similar spectra to Baltic amber or succinite, in North America and Greenland, while Savkevich would extend this to Asia. There is no reason at all for the same type of tree not to have grown in widely separated areas of the world.

Thin-layer chromatography

This method relies on achieving a separation of the various chemical components of a resin in solution, by virtue of the different speeds with which they are carried through a 'stationary phase' or a specially prepared mixture of absorbents (silica gel, cellulose, alumina and diatomaceous earth).

The chromatograms are made on glass plates previously coated with silica gel containing a fluorescent indicator. The process uses a developing solution of ethyl acetate in benzene, and the plates are finally sprayed with a solution of dichlor-fluorescin in isopropyl alcohol and viewed under long- and short-wave ultraviolet light (*Figure 15.1*).

Thin-layer chromatograms were used by Frondel (1969) to link the fossil resins of Richmond, Surrey, and Whetstone with those of Highgate copalite and glessite. All chromatograms were remarkably similar to that of *Bursera bipinnata*: 'Very similar yet distinguishable from those of the Bursera group, were the chromatograms of the fossil elemi Guayaquilite from Ecuador ... which was more like that of *Protium heptaphyllum*.'

Rottländer (1970) cited thin-layer chromatography as a method for distinguishing between copal and gedanite, as he considered that they could not be differentiated using infra-red spectrometry.

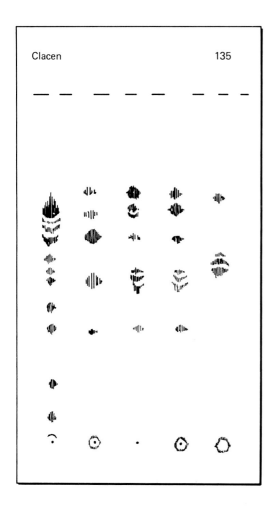

Clacen   135

Figure 15.1 Typical results from thin-layer chromatography showing (from left to right): resin, gedanite, copal I, copal II, reduced amber (Rottländer, 1970).

Savkevich (1981) does not mention these earlier authors, but notes that the work by Lebez (1968) has been shown by Kucharska and Kwiatkowski (1979) to be invalid, as the differences obtained by thin-layer chromatography in this case were apparently due to different degrees of oxidation and not to differences in geographic origin.

Mass spectrometry

This method involves the analysis of resin by electromagnetic separation of its ions: 1 mg of amber is vaporized by heating to 200°C in a vacuum. This is then subjected either to electron bombardment or field ionization in order to produce charged species from the original molecules. These charged particles are accelerated by an electric impulse and then passed through a magnetic field, which has the effect of changing their path from a straight line to a curve as some particles have a greater mass than others.

The ionized molecules of different resins picked up by the spectrometer show peaks in different areas of the mass spectrum because they have been separated according to this mass/charge ratio. For example, Baltic amber exhibits peaks at 92 and 101 cm^{-1} etc., Sicilian amber peaks at 115 and 204 cm^{-1} etc. (*Figure 15.2*) and Romanian amber at 190, 191 and 192 cm^{-1} etc. (Mischer, Eichhoff and Haevernick, 1970).

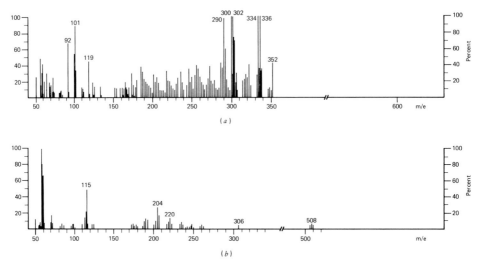

Figure 15.2 Typical results from mass spectrometry of amber specimens using field ionization: (a) field ionization of Baltic amber, (b) field ionization of Sicilian amber (Mischer, 1970).

Usually, samples appear to show little difference whether taken from the centre or the surface of a resin. However, the equipment necessary for this type of analysis is not widely available; it is sophisticated, costly and gives results that may be difficult to interpret.

Differential thermal analysis

This is used to investigate and identify the action of heat on resins. For example, a sample of 300 mg is heated in a closed tube or inert atmosphere and weighed at each 10°C per minute increase from room temperature to 620 or 1000°C. The reactions that give out heat are shown as upward peaks on a graph, while those reactions that absorb heat are shown as troughs.

The higher proportion of volatile components found in modern resins when compared to fossil resins shows as an increase in trough intensity over a lower temperature range.

Thermal characteristics were used by Broughton (1974) to differentiate between Atlantic coastal plain fossil resins and those from other geographic regions (*Figure 15.3*). This had not been proved conclusively with infra-red examination.

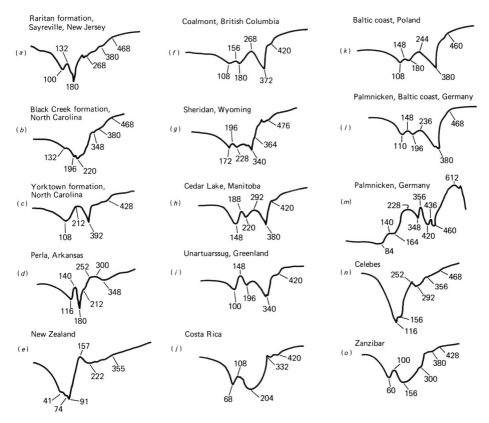

Figure 15.3 Differential thermal analysis was used to distinguish Atlantic coastal plain fossil resins from those of other geographical regions. Exothermic thermal curves peak upwards, the endothermic peaks project downwards (Broughton, 1974).

Emission spectrometry

This form of laboratory test has more in common with gemmology than the others in this chapter as gemmologists are familiar with the hand-held spectroscope. However, for emission spectrometry the sample is heated to a high temperature, and the atoms or molecules thus excited by this energy input can be identified by the wavelengths of light that they absorb or emit.

By recording and analysing which elements are present in a given sample, one can attempt to differentiate between resins from different locations. However, there are two major difficulties with emission spectrometry as a form of analysis. Each sample will reflect a very local variation as it will have been influenced by its immediate environment of burial, and published reference values show very large ranges. Samples must be taken from the interior of the resin to avoid contamination.

Neutron activation analysis

This is a complex and expensive form of analysis using trace element content to identify the geologic origin of ambers (as does emission spectrometry) which, although sensitive for some less common elements, requires access to a nuclear reactor.

Neutrons are used to bombard atoms, thus forming radioactive nuclides, which can be detected and identified. According to Das (1969), one would expect to find 200 parts per billion of gold in Baltic amber and 600 parts per billion in Sicilian amber, while Baltic amber contains 10 parts per million of sodium and Sicilian 1500 parts per million.

X-ray diffraction

This method permits the exact determination of the structure of molecules because crystal lattices act as diffraction gratings. The rows of atoms have spacings of a few Ångstrom units, which are comparable with the wavelengths of X-rays. By computation it is possible to work out three-dimensional, electron-density maps of the solid lattice from the recorded X-ray patterns.

A sample of amber is powdered and spread on a slide or pressed into an aluminium holder. This is studied in the X-ray diffractometer using filtered copper X-rays.

Only a few fossil resins give an X-ray diffraction pattern sharp enough to be of any value. Among those that do are Highgate copalite, settlingite from Settling Stones (both from Britain) and guayaquillite from Ecuador. Frondel (1967a) found the Highgate copalite and guayaquillite patterns to be identical with that of the modern angiosperm *Protium* and *Bursera*. She continues: 'If the crystalline constituents represented by these patterns have a genetic significance, then possibly the Highgate Copalite and Guayaquillite have a common origin and may belong to the family of Burseraceae'.

Some time later, Frondel (1967b) went on to identify the constituent represented by this pattern as α-amyrin (*Figure 15.4*), and at this point the Baltic amber glessite was added to those of Highgate copalite* and guayaquillite – all three showing α-amyrin to be present. Glessite and succinite are found mixed in the blue earth of the east Baltic, even though they are apparently of different plant origins and come from different geologic periods.

Broughton (1973), using the same technique, added the sliced section to the variety of methods of preparation of resin prior to X-ray diffraction (*Figure 15.5*). He found that, when resins were tested that had been sliced to a thickness of 4–5 mm, a previously unrecorded peak between 29.42 and 11.04 Å became obvious in all the *fossil* resins tested. As expected, the peak was lost when the samples were powdered.

Oxidation, either natural or induced, reduces the intensity value of the patterns, but modern resins have very strong intensities. Broughton (1973) found it possible to

---

Highgate copalite is a coarse, friable brown resin found in clay pits. The following is of note: '... in the clay-pits of Leicestershire, Northamptonshire and many other counties ... the neighbourhood of London also affords us some that is tolerably fine. I have several fine specimens picked up in the tile clay-pits in the fields between Tyburn and the Kensington gravel pits, and have met with yet finer in the great tile clay-pit behind St. George's Hospital at Hyde Park Corner, one of which I have had wrought and wear in the head of a cane, near three inches long ... With us amber lies at considerable depths, in a stiff blue clay, and always among the common pyrites.' (Hall, 1748).

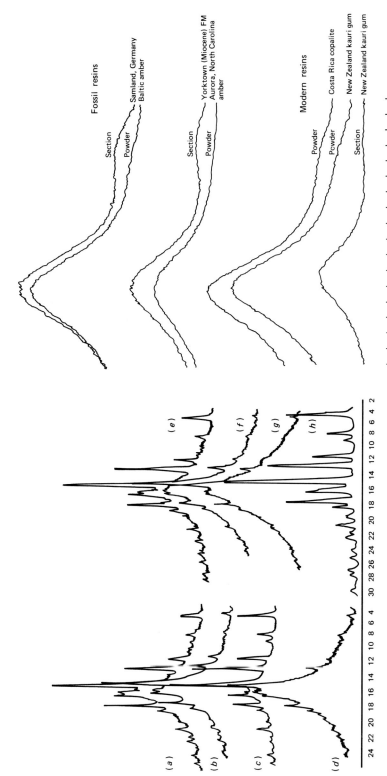

Figure 15.4 X-ray diffraction patterns of modern elemis (a–d), fossil elemis (e–g) α-amyrin (h). (a) Yucatan copal, (b) Tacamahaca resin, (c) Brazilian elemi, (d) *Bursera bipinnata*, (e) guayaquillite, (f) Highgate copalite, (g) glessite, (h) α-amyrin (Frondel, 1967).

Figure 15.5 Low-angle X-ray diffraction of fossil and modern resins and the comparative effects of sample preparation on peak intensity (Broughton, 1973).

distinguish between New Zealand kauri gum, which had an uppermost value of 94–100%, and other copals (Zanzibar, etc.) which had lesser values of 84–94%.

Bibliography

AGRICOLA, G., *De Natura Fossilium* (1546)

BECK, C. W., 'The amber trade', Savaria – Bulletin der Museen des Kohitats, Vas. 16. 1982, Internationales Kolloquim 1982. Bozsok-Szombathely (1983)

BERZELIUS, J. J., 'Einige Bermerkungen über den Bernstein', Vetensk. Acad. handlung (1827); reissued in *Pogg. Ann.*, **12** (1928)

BROUGHTON, P. L., 'Conceptual frameworks for geographic–botanical affinities of fossil resins', *Canadian Journal of Earth Science*, **11** (1974)

DAS, H. A., 'Examination of amber samples by nondestructive activation analysis', *Radiochem. Radioanal. Lett.*, **1**, No. 4 (1969)

FRONDEL, J. W., 'X-ray diffraction study of some fossil and modern resins', *Science*, **155**, No. 3768 (1967a)

FRONDEL, J. W., 'X-ray diffraction study of fossil elimis', *Nature*, **215**, No. 5108 (1966)

FRONDEL, J. W., 'Fossil elemi species identified by thin-layer chromatography', *Die Naturwissenschaften*, **5** (1969)

FUJINAGA, T., TAKENAKA, T. and MUROGA, T., 'Origin of the archeological amber in Japan, studied by infra-red spectra' [in Japanese], *Nihon Kagaku Kaishi*, **9** (1974)

HALL, J., *Natural History*, **I** (1748); in: Denny Papers, Mineralogy Library, British Museum (Natural History), London

HEYER, J. C. H., *Versuche mit Bernstein*, Erfurt (1787)

KUCHARSKA, M. and KWAITKOWSKI, A., 'Thin layer chromatography of amber samples', *Journal of Chromatography*, **169** (1979)

LANGENHEIM, J. H., 'Amber: a botanical inquiry', *American Association for the Advancement of Science*, **163**, No. 1872 (1969)

LEBEZ, D., 'The analysis of archeological amber from the Baltic Sea by thin layer chromatography', *Journal of Chromatography*, **33** (1968)

LÉ MERY, N., *Cours de Chemie*, Paris (1675)

MISCHER, G., EICHHOFF, H. J. and HAEVERNICK, T. H., 'Herkunftsuntersuchungen an Bernstein mit physikalischen analysenmethoden', *Jahrbuch des Römisch-Germanischen Zentralmuseums, Mainz* (1970)

ROTTLÄNDER, R. C. A., 'On the formation of amber from Pinus resin', *Archeometry*, **12**, (1970)

SAVKEVICH, S. S., 'Physical methods used to determine the geological origin of amber and other fossil resins: some critical remarks', *Physics and Chemistry of Minerals*, **7** (1981)

Chapter 16

Resins and their botanical parentage

Resins are synthesized in appreciable quantity by about 10% of the 280 plant families. Among the plants, primarily trees, that produce large quantities of resin, two-thirds of the species are tropical. In these tropical areas the angiosperm families Leguminosae and Dipterocarpaceae are noted for their copious resin production. All of the genera in coniferous families, which are primarily temperate, also synthesize resins. However, only the Pinaceae and Araucariaceae produce appreciable quantities (Langenheim, 1969).

Resin is produced in cells that usually line rounded pockets or elongated canals within the plant, but the exact cellular site where resins are synthesized is as yet unidentified. The spaces are created by the growth in cells which creates intercellular pockets of space, or the breakdown of cells into long cavities (*Figure 16.1*).

There are various opinions as to why a plant should produce resin, and the answer probably lies in a combination of some of these views:

(1) The production of resin could be a method of disposing of excess acetate.
(2) Resin could act as a growth inhibitor or stimulator. In pines, resin has been found to act as a growth inhibitor in high concentrations while in other trees, such as *Hymenaea courbaril*, the largest, most vigorous trees appear to produce the largest quantity of resin.
(3) The significance of resin is frequently attributed to protection against injury and disease inflicted by insects and fungi. Over millions of years components with the resin may have become modified, in that those trees which survived such attack produced the next generation, while those which succumbed obviously did not. 'High exudation pressures of resin, under the influence of water supply, have been shown to control bark beetle attacks. Insect-induced crystallation of *Pinus strobus* resin provides resistance to attack' (Langenheim, 1969).

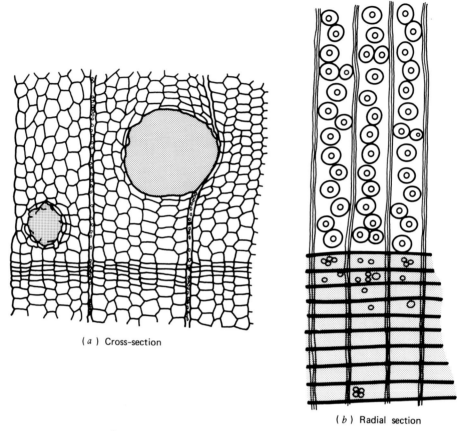

(*a*) Cross-section

(*b*) Radial section

Figure 16.1 A reproduction from Göppert and Menge, *Flora des Bernsteins* – for labels *see* that publication *British Museum* (*Natural History*), *London.*

Fossil resins

Fossil resin occurs in deposits ranging in age from Carboniferous (e.g. that from Northumberland, Britain), to Pleistocene (e.g. that from Tel Aviv, Israel), but it is found most commonly in strata of the Cretaceous and Tertiary periods.

The botanic origin of most ambers appears to have been coniferous until the Tertiary period. Since all the ambers under review in this book fall within the Tertiary, this particular situation is perhaps more complicated than might have been the case otherwise.

From the Tertiary period onwards the choice of resin producers opens out to:

(1) *Coniferous* – Pinaceae, Taxodiaceae (Sequoia, Taxodium) and Cupressaceae.
(2) *Angiosperm* – Hamamelidaceae (*Liquidambar*), Leguminosae (*Hymenaea, Copaifera,* etc.), Burseraceae (*Commiphora, Boswellia, Protium*) and so on.

The picture, so far incomplete, of the resins that are of interest to a gemmologist is as given in *Table 16.1.*

Figure 16.2 Cross-section of amber stalactite showing internal growth structure.

The origin of Baltic succinite

Authorities are still divided as to the origin of the most common amber used for gemmological purposes – Baltic succinite. One of the main problems is that modern and fossil resins are not identical, the latter having suffered the evaporation of terpenes as well as sesquiterpenes. It would also be expected, over the millions of years that have passed since amber was formed, that chemical alterations might have taken place due to heat, light, pressure, oxygen and water.

One area where there is agreement is that the presence of succinic acid in baltic amber is irrelevant to any search for botanical affinities in resins. 'Being nonterpenoid, however, succinic acid has been of little value in characterising resins' (Langenheim, 1969). 'Succinic acid occurs as a normal oxidation product of amber and is thus by no means indicative of its origin' (Rottlander, 1970).

In the late nineteenth century, Conwentz classified the source of amber as being in the genus *Pinus*, and in 1961, after more than 20 years of research, Schubert presented his work in which he proved that the assignment of the source of amber to the genus *Pinus* was 'without doubt'. Rottländer (1970) is convinced that amber is formed from abietic acid, which is a principal component of modern *Pinus* resin.

There are, however, certain problems about this theory. In the classic, chemical

TABLE 16.1. Resins of relevance to the gemmologist

Resin	Age	Reference	Botanical affinity
Burma (Hukawang Valley)	Eocene	Langenheim (1969)	—
Burmese (several varieties)	Post-Eocene Miocene Cretaceous	Schlee and Glöckner (1978)	
Baltic coast	Eo-Oligocene Miocene	Langenheim (1969)	Pinaceae (*Pinus*) – see text
Dominican Republic	Oligocene	Langenheim (1969)	—
Northern Cordillera	Lower Miocene	Rieppel (1980) Schlee *et al.* (1984)	Possibly *Leguminosae* and *Hymenaea*
Chiapas, Mexico (Simojovel Formation)	Oligo-Miocene	Langenheim (1969)	Leguminosae (*Hymenaea*)
Chiapas, Mexico	Upper Oligocene Lower Miocene	Hurd, Smith and Durham (1962)	—
Romania (Carpathian Mountains)	Miocene	Langenheim (1969)	—
Northern Sicily	Undetermined Tertiary	Langenheim (1969)	—
Sicily	Tertiary, exact age uncertain Possibly Miocene	Schlee and Glöckner (1978) Schlüter (1975)	

sense the fossil resins are unrelated to the modern pine resins (Broughton, 1974) and, according to tests, the amber source tree has a chemistry which on the whole resembles modern *Agathis* (family of Araucariaceae) more closely than modern *Pinus* (Mills, White and Gough, 1984–1985). No remains of Araucariaceae have been found with amber while fossil remains of a conifer (Pinites) are common along with other non-coniferous inclusions like oak hairs. However, trunk resins from genera of the coniferous families Araucariaceae, Taxodiaceae and Cupressaceae contain compounds which readily set under conditions of light and oxidation, and their resins set solid, usually quite soon after they have flowed from the tree.

A related compound is found in the several genera of the angiosperm Leguminosae family (*Hymenaea* and *Copaifera*). These characterize the resins from Central/South America and Africa. The Pinaceae are generally speaking low in these labdatrienoid compounds, their resin does not set quickly, and it is not found in a solid state in quantity.

The solution, as is so often the case, may be a compromise. 'The tendency is to consider it as rather a primitive type, representing an early stage in the developmental history of the Pinaceae which in their chemistry still retained archaic characteristics in common with the Araucariaceae' (Larsson, 1978).

Bibliography

BROUGHTON, P. L., 'Conceptional frameworks for geographic–botanical affinities of fossil resins', *Canadian Journal of Earth Science*, **11** (1974)

HURD, P. D. JR., SMITH, R. F. and DURHAM, J, W., 'The fossiliferous amber of Chiapas, Mexico', *Ciencia (Mexico)*, **21** (1962)

LANGENHEIMS, J. H., 'Amber: a botanical inquiry', *Science*, **163** (1969)

LARSSON, S. G., *Baltic Amber – A Palaeobiological Study*, Scandinavian Science Press, Klampenborg (1978)

MILLS, J. S., WHITE, R. and GOUGH, L. J., 'The chemical composition of Baltic amber', *Chemical Geology*, **47** (1984–1985)

RIEPPEL, O., 'Green anole in Dominican amber', *Nature*, **286** (1980)

ROTTLÄNDER, R. C. A., 'On the formation of amber from Pinus resin', *Archaeometry*, **12** (1970)

SCHLEE, D. and GLÖCKNER, W., 'Bernstein', *Stuttgarter Beiträge sur Naturkunde*, **C,** No. 8, Staatliches Museum für Naturkunde, Stuttgart (1978)

SCHLEE, D., (ed.), 'Bernstein-Neuigkeiten', *Stuttgarter Beiträge sur Naturkunde*, **C,** No. 18, Staatliches Museum für Naturkunde, Stuttgart (1984)

SCHLÜTER, T., 'Nachweis verschiedener Insecta-Ordines in einem Mittelcretazichen Harz Nordwestfrankreichs', *Entomologica germ*, **1** (1975)

SCHUBERT, K., 'Neue Untersuchungen über den Bau und Leben der Bernsteinkiefer', *Beihefte zum Geologischen Jahrbuch*, **45** (1961)

Chapter 17

Inclusions

'A drop of amber, from the weeping plant,
Fell unexpected, and embalm'd an ant;
The little insect we so much condemn
is, from a worthless ant, become a gem.'
(Rev. R. Graves, from *Martial Epigrams*, Book vi, Epigram XV)

Organic inclusions

Organic remains of insect or plant life that have been caught up in once-liquid resin are termed *inclusions*. The world of inclusions is one of advanced science, and the gemmologist is only expected to maintain a questioning mind with the × 10 lens. However, it is to be hoped that if something unusual does come his or her way it will be passed on to the palaeobotanist or palaeo-entomologist to make a specialist analysis.

Published material referring to organic inclusions falls into two categories.

'*A Scelionid wasp surviving unchanged since Tertiary* ... Abstract: *Palaeogryon muesebecki*, n.gen. and n.sp. (Scelionidae: Scelioninae), is described from both later Oligocene Mexican amber and recent specimens from Mexico. This is the first evidence in Proctotrupoidea of a species having survived unchanged during the past 30 million years. The fact is more surprising since this relict species constitutes a highly advanced (apomorphous) form of Scelionidae'.

(Lubomir Masner, Institute of Entomology, Czechoslovak Academy of Sciences, Prague. Reprinted from the *Proceedings of the Entomological Society of Washington*, **71,** No. 3, 1969)

or

'*Have you met George?* He's the smallest, oldest and cutest thing, and he's the reigning star of the gem and mineral show.' (George was a Gnat)

(*The Independent*, San Diego, 9 August 1956)

Unfortunately, the organizers of the show had not taken into consideration the easily induced crazing of the amber (or copal), for the article then continues: '. . . but pictures through the microscope are now very difficult because the amber surface has become quite checked probably because of the many hours of heating it withstood from the microscope illuminator lamp when being displayed to the public'.

Inclusions in amber vary in size from those only visible with enlargement to those about 4 cm in length. Most are a matter of millimetres and if an inclusion of a present-day sized moth or beetle is found, the piece is often a modern resin. Care must be taken with some of the lesser known nineteenth-century collections, for example the Perowne Collection of Ambers, Sedgwick Museum, Cambridge, Britain, where many of the inclusions described in amber during the past century are in fact inclusions in copal, or non-fossil resins.

The inclusions, both botanical and entomological, found in fossil resins have not shrunk to their small size: it is simply that the larger species managed to extricate themselves from the sticky resin before it overwhelmed them. Under a microscope there is often evidence of quite a struggle from insects before their death; indeed, this can often be useful evidence when querying the authenticity of the inclusion (*Figure 17.1*). Macabre relics of limbs or other parts of anatomy indicate the specimens either managed to escape or were eaten *in situ*. A milky residue can sometimes be seen surrounding the insect, especially at the mouth or anus, as evidence of exhudation under stress or chemical change. Likewise with plants, larger pieces of debris would not have been enveloped by the flowing resin, and surface-breaking inclusions would have been destroyed by ensuing microbiotic influences. This can be seen when amber appears with natural holes within, probably produced by twigs which once intersected it but which have long since decayed.

Although the ambers commonly used in jewellery – that is, those from the Baltic,

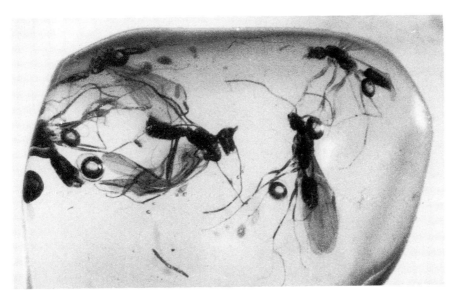

Figure 17.1 Evidence of the insect's struggle within amber. *Courtesy of Peter Read.*

Romania, Burma, Sicily and the Dominican Republic – are all of interest to those studying fossil insect or plant life, it is the older resins that house the real breakthroughs in our knowledge, for example those from:

(1) Lunz, Austria; Triassic: 225–231 million years old (Vavra, 1984).
(2) Southern Lebanon; Cretaceous: 125–130 million years old (Schlee and Glöckner, 1978).
(3) Cedar Lake, Manitoba, Canada; Upper Cretaceous: 70–75 million years old (McAlpine and Martin, 1969).

The first book devoted to inclusions in amber appears to be the *Historia Succinorum Corpora Aliena Involventum*, by Nathanial Sendel, published in Leipzig in 1742. Other publications, of a more specialized nature, followed throughout the nineteenth century, e.g. Maravignac, C., 'Lettre sur les insectes trouves dans l'ambre de Sicile', *Revue Zoologique*, **1**, pp. 168–171. In 1883, Göppert and Menge published *Die Flora des Bernsteins* (Coniferous inclusions) and the companion volume, published three years later, by Conwentz, dealt with angiospermous inclusions (*Figures 17.2* and *17.3*).

The number of inclusions, both of flora and fauna, found within amber is immense. However, the pure scholastic desire for research has often been thwarted by less noble ambitions of power and economics. The 2000 Baltic inclusions investigated by Berendt in Königsberg, in 1830, have been split up between Göttingen, Berlin and London, and it is only in the mid-1980s that sufficient pressure has been mounted by scientists, on the Dominican Republic, for a system of analysis of inclusions to be properly organized to replace the previous somewhat haphazard method used by the Department of Agriculture in Florida for investigation (Rice, 1980).

One of the foremost centres in the world today for the identification of insect inclusions is the Staatliches Museum für Naturkunde in Stuttgart. Here Dr Dieter Schlee, through his frequent publications, has brought the world of inclusions, especially those from the Dominican Republic, to a wider audience than ever before, and his books have set a standard of colour photography yet to be bettered (Schlee and Glöckner, 1978; Schlee, 1980, 1984).

The amount of work being carried out on amber inclusions is perhaps surprising to the gemmologist. A recent publication from Stuttgart – a bibliography of Coleoptera (beetles) in amber and copal – listed over 300 publications. The papers orginated in Berkeley, Berlin, Boston, Breslau, Brussels, etc. and show the world-wide interest in this very specialized form of preservation of fossils (Spahr, 1981). One paper tends quickly to follow another, this type of work being very rewarding as amber has often preserved minute inclusions in perfect detail. The sample list which follows is from the Entomology Research Institute in Ottowa:

(1) Richards, W. R., Entomology Research Institute Research Branch, Canadian Department of Agriculture, Ottawa: Systematics of fossil aphids from Canadian amber (Homoptera: Aphididae)', *The Canadian Entomologist*, **98**, No. 7 (July 1966). Five Cretaceous fossil aphids are described. All are new species and none is referable to an extant genus.
(2) McAlpine, J. F. and Martin, J. E. H., 'Systematics of Sciadoceridae and relatives

Family CUPULIFERAE

(*a*) Quercus trichota Casp. var. macranthera Conw.

(*b*) Quercus subglabra Casp.

(*c*) Quercus taeniato–pilosa Conw.

(*d*) Quercus piligera Casp.

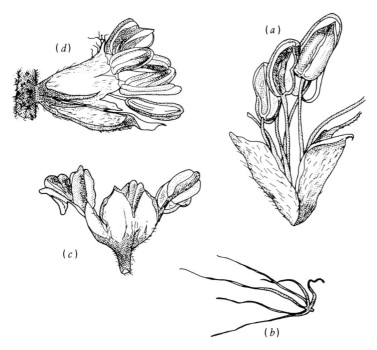

Figure 17.2 A reproduction from Conwentz, *Flora des Bernsteins*, Vol. II – for labels *see* that publication British Museum (Natural History), London.

with descriptions of two new genera and species from Canadian amber and erection of family Ironomyiidae (Diptera: Phoroidea)', *The Canadian Entomologist*, **98**, pp. 527–544 (1966).

(3) Teskey, H. J., A new soldier fly from Canadian amber (Diptera: Stratiomyidae)', *The Canadian Entomologist*, **103**, 1659–1661 (1971) The first pre-Tertiary record of this family.

(4) Hamilton, K. G. A., 'A remarkable fossil Homopteran from Canadian Cretaceous amber representing a new family', *The Canadian Entomologist*, **103**, pp. 943–946 (1971).

What is important to the layman about these findings is that quite often pieces of these rarer ambers (remember Canadian amber from Cedar Lake is estimated at 70–75 million years of age and is thus of an age when many of the modern insect families

Family CUPULIFERAE

(*a*) & (*b*) Quercus microgemma Conw.

(*c*) Quercus macrogemma Conw.

(*d*) Quercus subsinuata Casp.

(*e*) Quercus Meyeriana Ung. var. denticulata Conw.

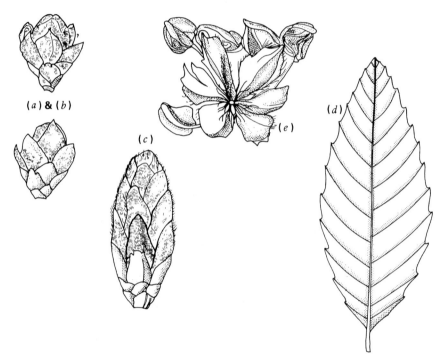

Figure 17.3 A reproduction from Conwentz, *Flora des Bernsteins*, Vol. II – for labels *see* that publication. *Natural History Museum, London.*

were probably still evolving) are retained by the public as curiosities, and are often not properly investigated. Regrettably, there is no treasure trove law that can be applied to resins.

   Perhaps the most exciting breakthrough in the 1980s, with regard to organic inclusions in amber, has been the location of soft tissues mummified within a fossil fly from the Baltic, and therefore approximately 40 million years old. Scientists at the University of California at Berkeley have conducted intensive research on the fly – a female fungus gnat – and consider that the tree sap itself penetrated the body cavity and that some of its constituents, namely sugars and terpenes, might have combined with the water in the fly's tissue to aid dehydration. Other chemical components within the amber or sap may have assisted preservation. According to newspaper reports (but not in the original scientific paper) it is hoped to extract DNA from the cells to attempt to grow genetic material from this 'fossil'.

Inorganic inclusions

Care must be taken with the cursory identification of inclusions so that inorganic inclusions like bubbles, especially those subsequently filled with metallic matter, or water, are not mistaken for plant or animal debris. Inorganic inclusions have an interest in their own right but to date have not been studied extensively, with a few exceptions (Flamini *et al.*, 1975). This type of included matter appears to be of particular interest to those practising homeopathy, who are looking for trace elements within the resin. There is no such inclusion as the 'lily-pad' or 'nasturtium leaf' – these are simply discoidal stress rings, caused by heating the resin either naturally or as part of a production process.

Bibliography

CONWENTZ, D. H., *Die Angiospermen des Bernsteins*, Danzig (1886)

FLAMINI, A., GRAZIANA, G., and GRUBESSI, O., 'Inorganic inclusions in amber', *Archeometry*, **17** (1975)

GÖPPERT, H. R. and MENGE, A., *Die Flora des Bernsteins*, Danzig, in 2 vols (1883)

MCALPINE, J. F. and MARTIN, J. E. H., 'Canadian amber – a paleontological treasure-chest', *The Canadian Entomologist*, **101** (1969)

POINAR, G., 'Ultrastructure of 40 million year old insect tissue', *Science*, **215** (1982)

RICE, P., *Amber. The Golden Gem of the Ages*, Van Nostrand Reinhold, New York (1980)

SCHLEE, D., *Bernstein-Raritäten (Farben, Strukturen, Fossilien, Handwerk)*, Staatliches Museum für Naturkunde, Stuttgart (1980)

SCHLEE, D., 'Bernstein-Neuigkeiten', *Stuttgarter Beiträge zur Naturkunde*, **C,** No. 18, Staatliches Museum für Naturkunde, Stuttgart (1984)

SCHLEE, D. and GLÖCKNER, W., 'Bernstein', *Stuttgarter Beiträge zur Naturkunde*, **C,** No. 8, Staatliches Museum für Naturkunde, Stuttgart (1978)

SPAHR, VON U., 'Bibliographie der Bernstein unde Kopal-Käfer (Coleoptera)', *Stuttgarter Beiträge zur Naturkunde*, **B,** No. 72, Staatliches Museum für Naturkunde (1981)

VÁVRA, N., 'Reich an Armen Fundstellen: Übersicht über die fossilien Harze Osterreiches', *Stuttgarter Beiträge zur Naturkunde*, **C,** No. 18, Staatliches Museum für Naturkunde (1984)

Appendix 1: Geologic ages

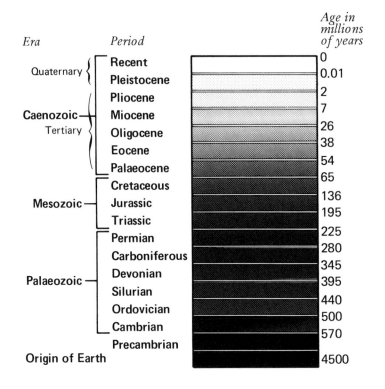

Era	Period	Age in millions of years
Quaternary {	Recent	0
	Pleistocene	0.01
Caenozoic— { Tertiary {	Pliocene	2
	Miocene	7
	Oligocene	26
	Eocene	38
	Palaeocene	54
Mesozoic—	Cretaceous	65
	Jurassic	136
	Triassic	195
Palaeozoic—	Permian	225
	Carboniferous	280
	Devonian	345
	Silurian	395
	Ordovician	440
	Cambrian	500
	Precambrian	570
Origin of Earth		4500

Appendix 2: Amber in the USA*

Amber has been found in 20 states within the USA. Since it is frequently found in connection with coal beds, more amber will certainly be uncovered in the future as the great US coal reserves are developed. It is not found in locations which are prospected for other gems and, since mining companies are not interested in investigating or mining anything but saleable coal (or sand or marl), it seems likely that much material has been passed up.

Amber from the USA is believed to have come from a now-extinct tree similar to the white cedar, but there are exceptions since all American amber does not belong to the same geologic time period.

Besides being found in conjunction with coal seams, amber may be found in sands, gravels, clays and marls. It is rather fragile and can easily be destroyed by the heavy machinery normally used in the USA in such areas. Amber is unique in that it is a gem which is of plant origin and may also represent the animal kingdom in its inclusions.

Amber in the eastern USA

Amber was found in New Jersey as early as 1792, according to Kunz. Large pieces were found in lignite beds near the Delaware river. The use of one large piece for a cane head was recorded. Later, amber was found in many of the marl pits of the state, which were mined for fertilizer. At one time the area of New Jersey that stretches from Middlesex County through Salem County was known as the major amber source of the USA. Many pounds of amber were taken from a single spot on the Shark River in the middle of the last century. The New Jersey amber that has been dated is from the Cretaceous, as is much of the amber of the west.

New Jersey amber has been found near Harrisonville, Trenton, Vincentown and

*Extracted from: Zeitner, J. C., 'Amber and jet', *Lapidary Journal* (April 1981).

Cliffwood. The amber has varied considerably in colour, size and inclusions, although generally the resin was said to be redder and darker than Baltic amber.

Another eastern locality is Anne Arundel County, Maryland. Both highly translucent amber and opaque amber have been found in this county. A late nineteenth-century find was on the steep banks of the Magothy River at Cape Sable. The cloudy amber was concentrically banded in colours of yellow, grey and brown. The transparent yellow amber was found only in small and scarce pieces. Amber was also reported from a lignite bed near Baltimore. Fossil leaves are reported in the lignite where the amber of Anne Arundel County was found and, in conjunction with the lignite, small branch-like pieces of jet were found.

Amber has been found in the sands of Coffee Bluff on the banks of the Tennessee River in Tennessee. The bluff is a landmark in northern Hardin County and is near Coffee Landing in the Milledgeville area. Milledgeville is on highway State 69 and only marked trials lead to Coffee Bluff. Rather small pieces of opaque to semi-translucent amber were found. The amber was cinnamon in colour, and was said to date from the Cretaceous period.

North-eastern states which have been the scenes of amber discoveries are New York, where the material was found on Staten Island, and Massachusetts, where amber specimens were recorded from Martha's Vineyard, Gay Head and Nantucket. They are listed as being of Tertiary origin.

Both of the Carolinas have yielded amber. Small pieces have been found near Myrtle Beach and Georgetown, South Carolina, in the phosphate pits. Poorly preserved petrified wood was found in the same area. Locations in North Carolina are near Greenville and Washington. Amber was found in phosphates near Aurora in a spot being prospected for fossils.

Nodules of amber have been found in the clays of Mississippi. A few fair-sized masses weighing several ounces were found in Tallahatchie and Tishimongo Counties in the rolling and wooded northern part of the state. The largest mass was in a clay pit in Tallahatchie county.

A find in Delaware is known. The late Walter Nydegger of West Virginia had a piece of amber and a piece of jet from his state. Isolated amber finds have reportedly been made in Kentucky and Ohio.

Amber west of the Mississippi River

A recent significant find of amber was made in Arkansas. It may be the largest documented find in this country. The large deposit was in the pits of the Acme Brick Company of Malvern, Arkansas, in Hot Spring County south-west of Little Rock. Thousands of pieces were collected in the beds of sand, clay and lignite. Many pieces were of large size and were translucent. With a large proportion of the pieces were beautifully preserved inclusions of plant and animal fossils. University of Iowa graduate student in geology, Royal Mapes, presented an important collection of this amber to the Museum of Comparative Zoology.

Earlier finds in Arkansas have been in a railway cutting near Gifford, also in Hot Spring County and on the shore of Lake Hamilton in Garland County.

Texas has recorded amber of the Cretaceous period from outcrops near Eagle Pass, a small city in Maverick County on the Rio Grande. I have also seen Texas amber reportedly found in a coal seam north of Beaumont, and from a sand and clay pit near Victoria. There are an increasing number of operating lignite mines in the state and these should be watched for both amber and jet.

Kansas has Cretaceous amber in the lignite beds of the Smoky Hill River in the northern part of the state. Five miles south of the little community of Carneiro in Ellsworth County, George Jelinek found a deposit of yellow brown amber, some cloudy and some translucent. Some of the pieces were 10 cm in diameter. The Kanopolis Dam has flooded this area.

Cretaceous amber was discovered in South Dakota recently by Texas scientist and art student James Ross. The amber occurred in a seam of dark, poorly consolidated fossiliferous material near a river in the western part of the state. The site, noted for its fossils, is in rugged and remote country. The surface finds of amber were mostly small but of rich colours. The exterior of most nodules was checked or crazed, but broken pieces showed bright translucency. No attempts had been made to explore the extent of the deposit. Several small plastic bags full had been collected. We burned a tiny chip of amber. It dissolved into a dark sticky goo releasing a pungent pine odour.

Maxine Wilson of Murdo has a piece of amber from the Missouri river. Mr Jennewein of Bison had amber from near a location formerly known as Fire Steel, South Dakota, where there was once a lignite mine.

Wyoming strip mines near Rawlins in Carbon County once yielded a small amount of amber. A recent report is of an isolated amber find in the coal mines near Gillette.

Small amounts of amber have come from several of the coal fields of Colorado. Some of the discoveries were in Boulder County and Larimer County on the east slope of the rockies, and others were near Walsenburg and Trinidad in the southern part of the state.

In New Mexico, amber has been found in the coal beds near Raton in Colfax County. Fine lumps of amber were found in the poorer seams of coal. Most pieces are in the hands of private collectors in the region. The amber is reported to be translucent and of excellent colour. Another New Mexico location is in western McKinley County near Gallup and Thoreau. Coal and peat areas near La Ventana near Cabezon have also produced minor amounts of amber. Other finds have been made in San Juan County in coal seams.

A few of the mines in Utah have produced small pieces of amber. These have been mainly from the coal seams of Wayne County.

Numerous occurrences of amber have been recognized in coal beds in King County Washington. Associated with the Eocene Age deposits were pieces of carbonized wood. A reported location is near Auburn, with another near Preston. Webster mentions amber in Ventura County, California.

Alaska has more historic uses of amber than our other states, as the Eskimos used large pieces of good-quality amber for many ornaments for hundreds of years. (We have a piece of Alaskan amber in our collection brought to us by a teacher from Barrow. It had been worked, polished and drilled.) The Eskimos used amber for beads, amulets, carvings, religious items, pendants and other uses, both decorative and utilitarian.

Apparently amber deposits were known by primitive people over wide areas of Alaska. Some of the locations are in north-west and in northern Alaska, and others are as far south as the Aleutians and Unalaska Island. Much of the amber is associated with coal beds. A bay in southern Alaska is named Amber Bay. The Cretaceous amber is found in place in weathering shales and coal seams, and as float on many shores. Some of the Alaskan amber is remarkably clear and richly coloured, ranging from honey to almost black.

The locking up of much of Alaska in the Wilderness system may leave the status of Alaskan amber at the *status quo*, but there are probably many undiscovered amber sites in this large state.

The mining of gems and ornamental stones by American Indians*

Amber was commonly used by the Eskimos and the Indians of Alaska and British Columbia, the Aztecs and Mayans, the Peruvians and the Indians of Santo Domingo and the Lesser Antilles and Colombia. A fossil gum was also used by the Brazilian Indians and a fossil resin closely resembling amber has been found in Mound Builder mounds in Ross County, Ohio. Reported occurrences of amber artefacts in Virginia and Tennessee may or may not be authentic.

The Eskimos of Point Barrow find from time to time amber on the beach and use it rough as amulets and rarely cut it into beads. It is called *auma*, i.e. 'a live coal' – a descriptive figure of speech. Ernest de K. Leffingwell saw the Point Barrow natives 'pick up a few pieces [of amber] a quarter of an inch in diameter from the protected beaches between Harrison and Smith Bays'. The Eskimos also obtained amber for beads from the alluvium of the Yukon delta and from the Tertiary formations of the Fox Islands. The Koniagas of Kodiak Island prize labrets, ear ornaments and pendants of amber which at times, particularly after earthquakes, are said to be thrown up on the south side of the island. Broken beads and pieces of amber are placed on the graves of the wealthy. It is also an important, though rare and costly, article of commerce among them. That amber was widely traded among the Eskimos long ago is shown by the presence of beads and uncut lumps in Thule culture ruins (about AD 600–1600) at Naujan on the shore of Fox Channel. Amber beads said to be of Asian origin were found in an Aleutian grave on Unalaska Island.

Amber and labrets of amber were among the tribute to be paid Montezuma by certain of the districts of Mexico, particularly the cities on the Atlantic coast and of Chiapas, a present-day locality. In Aztec times it was an important article of commerce. Sahagun reports that amber was obtained by the Aztecs from 'mines in the mountainous country'. Clavigero reports that it was used as an ornament mounted in gold.

*Extracted from: Ball, S. H., *Anthropological Papers*, No. 13, Smithsonian Institution – Bureau of American Ethnographs, Washington, DC (1941).

Appendix 3: Infra-red spectra of amber samples

Some thousands of infra-red spectra need to be taken before patterns of similarity can be ascertained. The following are examples showing spectra from amber of known origin (spectra courtesy of Gary Jones, British Museum (Natural History).

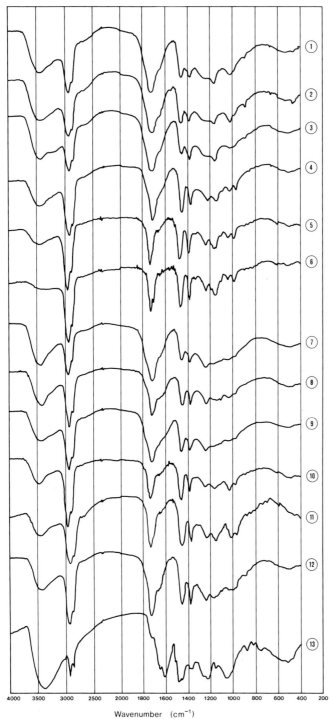

1 Baltic succinite: deep clear yellow bead.

2 Baltic succinite: dull, cloudy yellow bead.

3 Baltic succinite: clear, sherry coloured with large-scale crazing.

4 Oriental: Burmite clear, mid-sherry amber. Carved figure.

5 Oriental: dark clear, polished modern cabochon 'from China'.

6 Oriental: light, clear, polished modern cabochon 'from China'.

7 Sicilian: polished sherry-coloured amber.

8 Sicilian: sherry-coloured clear, rough.

9 Sicilian: dark red, rough.

10 Romanian: Buzau Province; dark, clear yellow, typically cracked internally.

11 Romanian: Buzau Province; light clear yellow, cracked internally.

12 Dominican: green-yellow.

13 Phenolic thermosetting resin (cross-linked by heating). Cloudy yellow.

Wavenumber (cm⁻¹)

Index